DATE DUE

29 DEC 1992	12 JAN 2010	
13 FEB 1996	- 8 MAR 2013	
2 1 MAY 2002		
- 5 AUG 2002		
27 SEP 2002		
0 1 AUG 2003		
1 5 NOV 2005		
18 MAY 2007		
2 7 FEB 2014		

2519

DOIN WILDCAT

By same author writing as Colin Johnson

Wildcat Falling
Long Live Sandawara
Doctor Wooreddy's Prescription for Enduring
*   the Ending of the World*
The Song Circle of Jacky and Selected Poems

DOIN WILDCAT

A Novel Koori Script
As constructed by

MUDROOROO NAROGIN

HYLAND HOUSE

First published in 1988 by
Hyland House Publishing Pty Limited
10 Hyland Street
South Yarra
Melbourne
Victoria 3141

Creative writing programme assisted by the Literature
Board of the Australia Council, the Federal Government's
arts funding and advisory body.

AUSTRALIA
COUNCIL

National Library of Australia
Cataloguing-in-publication data:

Narogin, Mudrooroo, 1938–   .
   Doin Wildcat.

   ISBN 0 947062 45 9.

   1. Wildcat falling (Motion picture). I. Title.

791.43'72

Jacket by Lin Onus
Typeset by Solo Typesetting, South Australia
Printed by Macarthur Press Pty Ltd,
Parramatta, N.S.W.

CONTENTS

To Jayne Lesley for inspiration

I
PRISON

ONE

'What the fuck am I doing among you Aussies, anyway,' the Yank protests.

I stare at the middle-aged guy. Ee looks more like some sort of shifty-eyed used car dealer than a filim director, but is credentials are A1, an ee is trying to be one of us. At this very moment is big splayed ands are desperately tryin to keep three balls circlin through the air. I stand right in front of the crowd of Kooris an call out: 'Use yer other two!'

Someone from the mob mocks me up: 'Ee's jugglin with is balls.'

Our raucous laughter causes im to break is concentration. A ball falls to the floor an rolls away. The other two follow it. 'Fuck,' ee exclaims.

Ee's brought us ere to make the filim of me novel. Is name's Al Wrothberg, a joke in itself. Ee's already told us that it means 'Anger of the Mountain', or some such shit. Well, no skin off our noses. We elect to believe im, after all ee is the biggest an whitest director/producer we've ever seen, an come all the way from America to spend big bucks an mix with us Abo's to make a filim based on me book. Ee's even told me that, as a special concession to 'you people', ee would allow me — the writer — to be on the set to see ow a movie is put together. Must've thanked im for this great favour, for ee went on further to tell me that ee even ad decided to go along with Aboriginal policy an accept one of us as trainee director to learn the ropes.

All this I takes in with a smile, not a grin, but a little twistin of the lips. Al, after all, is the bread and the butter of our movie, an I don't want to queer it for the others. We all know that ee's makin it for the money, that if ee's goin along with our whims, it's not because ee's white, but Jewish, an em people're supposed to ave suffered a bit like we ave, an this sometimes makes em sink all Jewish brown eyes into other people's sufferin, just to get a feel of what it's really like — em ghettoes, em murderings, em gas-ovens, those uniformed bastards standin over yuh with sticks an guns, an clubs an words. Yeah, em Jews ave known it too, so we decide that ee's not just another Gubba, a Watjela wantin to rip us off, but a Jew, an that means sufferin an dispersal an all that. Well, it does, don't it?

Feel me thoughts turnin sour. Yuh know ow it is when you've bin drinkin a little too long an a little too much an things just roll over on their fronts instead of their backs an the dog is ready to snarl, ready to bite. Just like that an you've got to get some relief. Light relief — which is provided by our trainee director, some smart Koori from Sydney, who is sometimes bright, sometimes mellow, sometimes just on old — but when ee's ad a charge . . .

Fuck it, this ol place is givin me the shits, givin me all those feelins that ave just lain inside of me ready to take old. Yuh know, they weren't content to buy me book, get me to write the script an all that, but I ave to be invited along to me ol prison ome of many long years — some home — an now to be a ome for no one any more, except us, this filim mob taking advantage to do a little time. Last sentences bein served in the ol boob, short timers getting a taste of what it was like. An then, yuh know what? They makin it into a museum, a bloody museum dedicated to their colonial arts an crafts. Some arts an crafts alright. All bloody with the blood of both black an white prisoners cryin for a little rest, for a smoke, for just one drink before they go down the tube rail into some sort of ole. No sign of ell though, they ad that on this earth, an it would just be a oliday ome compared to what they ad to put up with ere.

So now I've come back for a last few days. A week at the most, do it standin on me ead, but I feel all the scars of those other days ache in me memory — that first long walk from the waggon into the receival centre where they stripped yuh an eye-fucked yuh, an washed yuh down with stinkin soap into rough clothin of grey or brown, an what were yuh? What were yuh? Nuthin mate! Nuthin, bradda! Nuthin, Kuda! A shit-scared eap of shiverin flesh. A kid of sixteen tryin to keep is bottom lip from tremblin an is eyes from droppin tears onto is tough little brown cheeks. God, I adn't even ad a woman then, or anythin like that. Goin almost straight from orphanage to prison don't leave yuh much room along the way to prong a collar or two, or even to get so charged that yuh were beyond it. Yeah, just a fuckin kid, but a Swan kid who could steal the pants off a drunk. Yeah, but ee got caught that time, got caught, as I'm caught in memories of those times, those times that enter into me as if it were appenin again, as it did appen again, an then again. But yuh never get over that first feelin — the feelins of a nuthin kid. Yeah, bradda, a shit-scared nuthin kid just born for the world to run over . . .

'Yuh know, there's this swimmin ole on the Murrum-bidgee river, right near to Canberra an they all go to swim there. Well, this Koori, this Aborigine, ee's taken there. Come to Canberra on some business an ad a day off, an some of the people ee met took im along. Well, ee's there, an ee sees this absolutely beautiful woman in a very spunky bikini. Well, ee looks, yuh know is eyes just about pokin outa is ead, an ee pushes it all down an goes up to er, very cool-like, an ee sez: "Excuse me, miss, you got any Aboriginal in you?" Well, she was brown from the sun an all that an she could of bin a Koori. Ee was new in Canberra an didn't know the local mob. Well, the woman was taken aback by is question, yuh know ow it is, but then she decided to be friendly an answered: "No!" Well, our Koori chap, ee thought ee ad a toe in the door, so ee put on is charm, an is best accent an replied: "Well, how would you like a little bit of Aboriginal in you?"'

Can't elp falling over meself at Kevin Coles little bit of fun. Ee's the trainee director, yuh know, an if ee's as good at directin as ee is at tellin em jokes, we'll ave a block-buster on our ands. An he knows just when to tell em too. Yer just standin there, feelin say a little down, or just lettin things build up inside yuh as I was just doin, when along ee comes an slips one into yer mind, an with a rush whatever was worryin yuh goes in a great roll of laughter, an yer ready to get onto somethin else, like slippin a little black to some woman.

I look around the room in which we're avin this party before shootin starts tomorrow. Lots and lots of bottles, some empty — but enough full to last out the night even at the rate these brothers an sisters are puttin it away. Well, no grog worries, an I turn me mind to what else but sex. If that's to appen it as to appen now before I get too pissed to get it up. These filim birds are somethin out of the ordinary, not somethin I even dream about screwin. A real stunner, but young, is perched all beautiful legs on the edge of a table, an by erself too. She is something to fly with. Might just go over there an see if the rest of the night will be taken care of. Worth a try. I'm used to knockbacks!

'Ey there!' Brown eyes fill mine with not much interest. But she's a stunner all right, brown lush skin sort of shiftin towards yuh. A garden to wander through slowly, but er voice as bin educated into that pose tone that sets these people way away from me in some distant land of limp ands an instant dismissal. 'You're the script writer,' she oozes out in carefully cultivated flowers that ave never bin touched by the wild grasses of the land. She's a garden all right, lush an carefully tended to be seen, admired, an with keep off signs everywhere. Well, maybe I can become the gardener? I've ad experience in that line of work. Maybe I should soften the soil with a joke? Maybe? — instead I sing a little bit of a song — old Koori song I eard from a bloke inside:

> Can't we ave a song about Australia,
> About the emu an the kangaroo,
> A song about the possum an the wattle blossom,
> A Koori kind of rag will do.
> Can't we ave a song about the old gum tree,
> All about our native land,
> Somethin original about us Aboriginal,
> A real Australian rag . . .

She looks at me, er brows archin in cultivated surprise an oozes, 'And a composer too!'

Things aren't goin too well. Worse, she begins to get me goat. I can't take this sort for long before I start funnin an tryin to take the micky outa them. Not really givin a damn now, I tell er Kevin's joke. She doesn't get it — at first, then gets it, then isn't so smug any more. Confusion marks er face. If she's goin to work with Kooris she'll have to get used to Kooris. Er eyes flicker an I know she wants to escape. I grin an sway pretendin to be more drunk than I am, then I slur out words to get her into action.

'Sorry,' I say. 'I'm pissed now, but just ang on over the next few days an I'll get sober enough to do a good job. With yer body, it's more than a lube yuh'll need.'

She's gone, leavin behind a wisp of perfume, an I feel a lust for er I adn't felt when I came on over. I also feel shame for pickin on er, but then what the ell? Me eyes don't skip after er. Time enough for that. I'm oldin a glass an that glass is just about full. I drain it, lettin the coolness sweep down me throat. Good drop of stuff, but it doesn't cool that feelin angin on down below. That's the problem with feelins. Yuh never know when they'll strike an for ow long they'll old on. Still, there's always the grog. I go an exchange me glass for a bottle. Won't need a refill for a long time. Still, that feelin drives me on. . . .

'So you play me mum? Don't look much like er, though —'

'What did she look like? You know I have to get into the part and start to feel what she went through?'

This woman is another stunner, but a Koori an that gives me an edge: I don't ave to think up smart questions an answers. An she's sexy too, seems to ooze that sex appeal. Maybe she'll be able to drive away any thought of that other one. I've bin told that she's fifty. Don't believe it, not with that body, not with those tits. But then I did ear that she's a bit funny, on some feminist kick, somethin like that. Yuh know, touched by the white wand of progress, but then what about me writin stupid books for some sort of livin. Well, she can be in the movie of me book. God, mummy!

'She was small, yuh know, small an dark with long black air that went down to er waist. She was beautiful . . .

I pass over the bottle to er. Suddenly I realise me mum wasn't like that the last time I saw er. I was rememberin er as a kid before they took me to the orphanage, not later, much later with the scars of jail on me, an a prison blues to mock me smart-kid street-scene act with white mates all ready to do a bust an dob me in for a lighter sentence. It was after she ad made it to the city an rented the small loneliness of a room far from ome an lations. She sat in that room with only a tiny radio for company. A small brown woman with sad grey air — nuthin like this body at me side. I feel the soft flesh of er breast pressin against me shoulder. Yuh know, I can't even remember the feel of me mother's breasts, or even remember em. All I know is the touch of any number of women like this one — though this one, I know as no promise in er flesh. These filim folk seem to be a bit like that, uggin an kissin, an not ready to give out.

I'm learnin, ain't I? — an on the first night too. Yuh see, I sit, I watch, I catch their ways. A bradda told me once that we ave two lives, that we are unters in this world, an to survive aveta learn ow to mimic, learn the art of camouflagin ourselves as we unt in the different worlds. Well, maybe it's like that, maybe it ain't. Still I aveta pretend to ignore that woman's breast, that Clarissa Egan's woman breast pressin against me side, as I tell er about me mum an ow strong she was an ow she fought to get a widow's pension to support us kids for the time they left us with er — an ow one by one we were taken to omes that were nowhere as feelin good as me mum's ome with essian sackin on the window, with rain sweepin in through the rusty tin roof, with lots of love an freedom to roam the bush until they come for us one day, two days, three days, an on the eighth day all us eight kids were up in those omes. I ope they tell it like it was in this movie. With that American Al swayin over Kevin who's tellin another of is jokes. The roar of laughter its me an I look up an into the eyes of that woman an the lust I feel stifles any laughter in me. It also wrecks me camouflage. I can feel that breast against me shoulder an I turn so that my body is against er body. I can feel me cock stiffenin an I know she feels it too.

'I want to fuck you,' I tell her, knowin it to be alf true.

'Yeah, you want to put yer penis in me vagina, I can feel that,' Clarissa replies in a filimic parody of a tough gin.

It puts me off. I want somethin a little more romantic, but then adn't I bin the same with the other one. We not chickens any more, an know what we want — maybe? . . . I ask er to come an see the prison garden with me. I know that garden. I was one of the ones that made it. We dug it out for a lousy 50 cents a week an a ration of tobacco. Well, it was out in the open an better than bein cooped up in the division all day. It was where I got me experiences in gardenin, an ow to make things grow.

'Not just now. There's no hurry. I'll keep you in mind if I decide to have a guy over the next week.'

'Thanks,' I say to er back, then say to meself 'Not if I

can elp it.' Still she's made me feel a bit wild, an I take me bottle an go off by meself. I walk towards that gate, that big gate. A while ago it swung open to eject me with enough sense to not want to go through it again. That was after the third sentence. Only a few days between em too. I wrote about those days in the book we're filimin. Wrote it ere in jail to fill in every ateful year of just wantin to get out an run an run away from all that urt, from that men's company of opeless braggin of jobs pulled an empty successes. After all, they were all inside with me, an did they ave that 'just a stupid kid' excuse? No, they didn't! They thought they were all super crims—an were lumbered for shop-busts. Rob a bank, they always said an few of em ever did, an those of us who did ended up ere with more years to count than I ad months in that first sentence. So much for big dreams!

I sit down on the kerb an eye that inside gate of bars. Yuh were driven through it in the waggon. Driven through it, to emerge into the feelin of dread pressin yuh down into the cold formalities numberin an abusing yuh in silence. Yeah, that was then, but now the screws are gone, an the prisoners, an all the pain that made this place a jail. I sit on earin a soft sobbin arisin from the stones around me, from the earth beneath me, from the bars, from the broken neck of the last anged man as the screw swung on is legs to correct a botched angin; earin the silence of the convicts screamin an beatin out on their tin plates a protest at legal murder. Please, let's forget about the illegal ones. Officer, let's forget, sir! I'm back again with nuthin but the memories of you in this place, an I've become a writer of a sorts an ave scripted a picture which'll show little of what I'm feelin—or maybe a lot! It depends on the movie an perhaps on Auschwitz an Treblinka, an a joke told by Kevin at the right time to turn the American guy's mind eyes around an onto the faces of ard-eyed guards murderin without mercy. Let's forget all that, bradda, while I sit still mindin me own business an lookin at that gate. It opened wide that first day they brought me ere, swung shut behind this dumb kid, with not stars, but loony tunes in his ears, an not even a woman or a silly drunken afternoon as memories to fill in those empty times a'ead of im.

This is where I'm at in me ead. Not a fit place for travellers, when Ernie comes along, sidles up as if ee's disturbin somethin, an finally sits down beside me with a full bottle of beer. I know that ee wants to ask me somethin. Ee's playin me in this filim, an no way could anyone play me. No way!

I turn to im an watch that carefree grin of is flicker across is face — an die. Ee still as is air in the careful permed curls ee fancies the girls fancy, an I wonder if ee'll get em cut for the prison sequence. I remember what they did to me air.

'Yuh know,' I say to him, 'yer air's all wrong for the times. It was the mid 'fifties an we were into D.A.s an Tony Curtis styles — all slicked back with grease an a curl danglin over the forehead. Yer know what the bastards did when I came in ere. I was escorted to the barber an a mean little screw stood an watched as ee run the clippers over me ead. I could've cried when I saw me curls tumblin to the ground. They fell all round me like dreams. I didn't take it lyin down though, an kept on tryin to grow em back, but that bastard of a screw kept on escortin me to the barber an I kept on avin no air — an no dreams. I knew what it was like when Samson woke up to find is locks all gone. There was some rule that a month or so before yuh were due for release, yuh could let your air grow, but I learnt it was a privilege when the day before I was due out, ee escorted me to the barber again. That's what they were like, the bastards!'

Ee finishes off is bottle, an I pass im mine. Ee takes a swig, then gives a alf apologetic glance at me, those curls swingin around to mask is face as ee says: 'Yuh know, the make-up girl'll fix up me air for the part. I don't want to lose it — might feel like Samson too. . . .' Then ee goes on to mention me script. 'Yuh know this character of yours, well, don't yuh think ee's a bit too quiet? Al's decided to make some changes to it. Nothin big, yuh understand. Jest lettin yuh know, so that yuh won't be too surprised when yuh see some parts are different from the way yuh wrote em.'

Ee passes the bottle back to me. I take a long swig that empties it, an toss it away with any ideas I might ave ad that they'd leave the script alone. I knew it wasn't done that way, an it isn't done that way. Well, fuck em, let em do what they want to do. Tired of the whole fuckin story anyway. What with the writes an the rewrites. The bottle rolls across the ground without breakin. I watch it, wonderin what to say to this kid who's never bin inside, never bin in on a bust, an never done nuthin much with is time until some producer or other picked im up an ee found imself in the movies. Not to ave bin in trouble is what I don't know about, just as I don't know ow to set about livin a normal life an never feelin the need to be constantly on guard — so what do I say to im? Tell im that the changes are okay, that yuh can't expect to ave an audience feelin sympathetic about an orphanage kid tossed out into the world with no knowledge of ow to make is way. I couldn't tell im about the stupid things I done, or ow that pride in being a Swan kid elped to pull me through? I look across at the wing of the main prison buildin juttin towards us. It's where the party is, an I need another bottle. It's also the Admin block an as we get up an walk towards it, I begin to tell im about the time when I stood in front of the prison magistrate, an ow then I wasn't actin timid, I was timid an — shit scared!

TWO

AL: Just hold that shot right in. Close up on his face. Aim for the mouth. I want his mouth to swell out of the screen. Right, this is a take. Cameras rolling, action!

The bloke playin the prison magistrate, clears is throat, an stares into the camera.

Magistrate: *You are charged with assault, with disobeying orders, and with insolence to an officer. How do you plead?*

AL: Cut, cut, that's getting near to how I want it. Now we'll go straight to the same shot of Ernie. I want those mouths to be emphasised. Ernie, kid, don't look mean, just bewildered, make it show in the mouth, but with a twist of toughness. You're a kid of seventeen, but you've seen it all. Right, that's good. This is it—cameras, action!

KEVIN: Give it a mouthful, Ern.
AL: Oh fuck, fuck, next we'll be having the writer having his say. Quiet on the set. This is it. Ready—now! Okay, okay, we'll try it again. Remember, Ernie, the mouth, the mouth, that's what I want, the mouth!

I'm watchin this, this filmin of the scene, an don't like

it. Im an is fuckin mouths. Then, Ernie asn't got his part eatin away at im. Christ, it's me on trial there, me as a kid. Ee as to give is bottom lip a tremble to show that shit-scared feelin, but then ee as to control it too. Ee's tough, ee won't let it out an reveal to the bastards what they're doin to im. Ee knows ow to ide is feelins, bin doin it all is life, it ain't nuthin new to im, but that doesn't stop the dread feelin from crampin up is stomach. No, it don't! an it's always like that — the next time is just as bad as the first time. That's got to be felt in this picture, got to be felt somehow. It's got to be like it was in the book, or was it like that in the book? Only know ow it felt in real life. Yeah the feelin of it.

Christ everythin is startin to get all mixed up — life, book an now filim. What happened, ow did it appen? So long ago, an now only the feelin remains true. Did it appen as I describe it in the novel? Nah, no way! It ad to be written like that to please em. Anyway can ardly remember why I was before the magistrate, or why I changed it when I came to write about it. Still, I must've ad a reason for tellin it ow it didn't appen. Yeah, remember now, wanted to get back at one of those screw bastards, a mean little cunt with a moustache an a chest of medals provin ee was in some kind of war. Only feelins are true an ee ated me as much as I ated im. Ee ad it in for me. Ee ated me guts an I ated his guts in return. Yuh know, yuh never could get the bastards in real life, so I ad to get me revenge in another way. I wrote im into the story an done there what I should've done to im in reality. Still there was that other thing I did, an that proves I wasn't running shit-scared all the time, that I could turn an snap an show the bastards that I meant business, but that was somethin else, not the book thing, not the filim thing. Yuh know, on the top landin, lookin down at the screw, a bucket of ot tea in me and, eavy an full an ot — real scaldin an all ready for that screw. Must've dreamt it often. The bucket over the landin, the liquid streamin as it cascaded down a regular waterfall to drench that screw an send him scaldin ome to mummy. Feelins is all that matter. An what we did do was better — better cause we did it all together an showed em that they couldn't mess around with us juveniles.

Remember it as if it appened yesterday. I wanta see that cell again; wanta feel me old mates around me. Ad enough of this judgement scene anyway. Ad enough judgements to last me for life. Christ, this filimin is a slow cut cut business, like they cuttin the flesh from me body. Suppose, later on they'll sew the pieces back together in a shape I most likely won't even like. Well, let it appen.

I ear Ernie say 'Dunno' as I drift outa the door. One thing I'm good at is driftin. Thought of meself as a black cat one time, just a flicker at the corner of someone's eye, at the corner of that lush-bodied girl's eye. Wonder where she is? She's not in this scene. Might meet up with er somewhere. Black cat on the prowl. Nah, I'll leave that to later, wanta see that cell, wanta renew me acquaintance-ship with part of me ol ome. I ear Ernie say 'Dunno' again, as they do another take. Yeah, I said that too. Playin dumb was part of me toughness, but that inner quakin soon changed it over to 'Guilty'. You never could win it over em. They soon made yuh say what they wanted yuh to say. . . .

A door at the eastern end of the Admin block leads into the Main Division of the buildin which runs north and south. Directly across it, on the other side, as if by plan is another door. I remember passin through that door more than a couple of times. It was always the same. Between two screws, esitatin at that door. The first time I didn't know what was on the other side of it. Us juveniles were kept in First Division which was for the short termers, an weren't allowed to mix with the ardened crims in the other divisions. But for all our separation we ad a fair idea of what went on be'ind the door. We ad eard those scary tales of blokes gettin bashed up in the punishment block. Thud, thud of fists sodden onto armless flesh. If I ad've really dropped the tea on that screw, it would've bin me for sure—thud, thud, sodden flesh shudderin under fists an boots. Afternoon delight an evenin delight an teach the bastard a lesson that'll make all of em others sit up as they listen to is screams. Never try to make yer mark on a screw, or they take yuh an mark yuh, until yuh bleed an shed blood, pissin yerself as yuh pass an examination yuh'll always remember—with self-loathin! So I never done, never took that examination. Those scary tales was enough for me—an for most of us. No one likes to be beaten into a white pulp, no one!

Well, yuh know, one screw, ee stopped right ere, just in front of the door. It's unlocked now, then it was locked, always locked just as all doors were locked. Prison is the sound of janglin keys an locked doors being unlocked then locked again. Yeah, it's loud like that. Well, one screw, ee opens that door, while the other one stands be'ind me, as if I could ever make a break from the Main Division piled igh with rows of locked doors an thick walls of stone. That day only one door was open an that door was for me. We go through. The first screw stops to lock it, the other walks a'ead of me. Bad sign that, nuthin be'ind to run through, nuthin be'ind except that screw lockin the only unlocked door. I face an iron gate, of course it is locked an must be unlocked. I march through, an stop for it to be locked, then pass down a narrow length of concrete box to another locked door, an then into another length of box this time with a row of doors locked on either side. Twelve of em, an one is for me! A screw opens it. I gape, for an alf metre be'ind is a locked door.

'Undress, you!' An they eye-fuck me as I strip down an stand there shiverin with more than cold. Then they open that other door to reveal a bare tiny cell. I am ordered to enter, an I enter. They search me clothes an fling em in after me. I stand there shiverin in that little concrete box. Igh on one wall is a very small barred window. The only light, the only friendliness as the door

slams, as the other door slams. As muffled steps drag
away, as another door slams. I am lonely as can be. I look
around at the walls, at the floor, at the shit bucket, at the
bible lyin on the floor. Too gloomy to read at first, but
when the sun is igh enough light scatters through the
tiny squares in the window to splatter on the floor.
Friendly light, even friendly bible. Fourteen days of
solitary an I'm ready to pray to the Lord. Pray an nuthin
appens until me time is up. Yeah, but thank the Lord, no
one came to belt me. That was somethin I could feel
grateful about. . . .

One day in eternity, the door clangs back. I blink up
into the startled eyes of the director. The whole camera
crew stare in at me.

'Ey, you okay,' Kevin asks me.

They all look at me anxiously. I get the feelin that I
must be appearin strange, yuh know, as if I ad just done
that fourteen days again. . . .

'Yeah, okay,' I mutter, gettin to me feet from the
position on the floor just under a ray of light. Feelin a
little dizzy an swayin too. Just before they came in, the
cell ad begun whirlin round an round, though me ead
was stayin still. Put it down to the drink or few I ad the
night before, manage a smile as I say that I ad bin relivin
old memories that ad got all mixed up with the aches of
last night's angover.

But Kevin continues to stare at me. Ee says: 'Yuh
know, there was the time one of me lations came to the
city. First time in the big smoke. We took im to this
department store. Big place with lifts an escalators. Leave
im standin in front of a lift. Yuh know, just leave im
there just to see what ee'd do. First time in is life ee's seen
one of em, so we put im in front of it, tell im to wait for
us, then go just a little bit away to watch. Ee stands starin
at those doors, watchin those doors openin an closin,
seein the people enterin an leavin. He stands, just
watchin, doin nuthin else but watchin. We go back to im,
an ee turns to us an says: "Yuh know I watchim people

go into that room. Go in, I watch, little time goes by, an doors open, then new people come out. Those people go in, new lotta people come out. Yuh know I look inside, no doors no windows, no way out, an those people go in an out come new people. They change into different people in there.'''

They all laugh at this. All except me. Yeah, people go into little rooms just like this one. They put yuh in these little rooms an then after a time, too long a time, they take yuh out, an yuh're changed, all different inside. That's what they did to me. They locked me away in this tiny cell, left me for a month an then came an took a new me out. A quieter an more passive me; a meaner an nastier me too. Well, fuck em, I say!

I push past the camera crew. Leave em to argue out the problem of settin up the cameras in such a confined space. It'll take em some time to do it, though not as long as it took me to figure out ow to handle the space an the silence, an the locked away feelin that made the big jail outside into some sort of freedom. Yeah, yuh could actually walk a good distance, actually leave yer division an go to church, ave a good sing along. Even receive letters, that is if anyone wrote to yuh. No one ever wrote to me, but what the fuck. I did a correspondence course an got letters every week. That's ow I got an education of a sorts.

No writing allowed in solitary though, nuthin allowed! Yuh there to be punished not for a Sunday school picnic. I walk away an out of that no-no place without a backward glance. It'll be the last time I'll be seein it. I never want to see it, to be in it again. I learnt me lesson there, yuh know, though I still aven't got on to why I was put in there that first time. I'll get to it, but first I wanta go to First Division an feel again that place. Get the memories started. Bit different now though. All the doors are unlocked. Few janglin key sounds'll ever be eard again, or maybe more seein it's goin to be a museum of a sorts, an they guard the iron relics of their past.

Great fuckin doors of darkened wood seal off the divisions, but the great bolts ave bin drawn back an the big brass Chubb locks are gone away with the keys. I turn south, push through one of those great doors. Let me feet echo back the cries of the prisoners as they move me through Second Division. It's all so changed, so different from that time when, just a stupid kid, I came into this place. Then I felt small an puny, lost in the ugeness of it all. On both sides four tiers of cells reach towards the distant roof rafters an daylight greys through an almost reaches me from the dirty squares of skylights. 'Sky light, sky bright, let me make it with my baby tonight.' An the central all then was never this narrow space, cramped between these four tiers of cells with the roof only about 18 metres or so above me ead.

Where as all that ugeness gone; where as all that cavernous space vanished to? Where, but into those years I ad added on to me youth. The prison was built in the 1880s, an it is small an cramped an narrow, never uge an spacious. But if it once ad seemed so to me, then ow small I must've bin; ow small to have found agrophobia in this claustrophobia.

Through another set of those thick wooden doors, an I'm in First Division. The next scene'll be shot ere, an they already ave selected a cell, one on the ground floor where there's enough room to manoeuvre the cameras. Some lights ave been set up around the cell door. It's not the right peter, but then what is the right peter for what never appened, though it appened in the book an'll appen in the filim. Any cell'll do for that tea bucket thing, that wish thing!

I stand right in the centre of the all, bend back me neck an look towards the top landin. Yuh can't see it. Yuh ave to go right to one side, against the opposite cell doors, then bend yer neck right back, but the chicken wire can be seen from anywhere. Ow could it not be, stretched across the bottom of the first landin. Stretched right across the main all so that no objects can tumble down, but there is that round ole still in it, that round ole made by the bucket rippin through to drench the screw with tea. The wire net stopped it for a single instant, givin im enough time to glance up an get the burnin liquid full in the mush . . . But it never appened, but it never appened, never appened like that. I never done it to im. Only gammon, a lie. Confused, I stare down at the grimy flagstones of the all. Us juveniles ad to get down an scrub those, yuh know. Get down on our ands an knees an scrub em into whiteness. Whites love whiteness, yuh know!

I look down at em an let the memories of us mob come outa that floor, outa the sweat soaked into the stone. I can see em as if today was yesterday. They were me mates, the only mates I ad in boob, an we fought an carried on an carved names into our skins, markin em deep with soot so that I'd always remember Eric, Chinky, Jack an Ralph who started the whole thing. In scrubbin that floor, we ad to use caustic soda an crawl in a line, an scrub an scrub an rub an rub, an why? — all because that mean fuckin screw ad decided that, after years of grey grime, it was time for the flagstones to shine as Persil-white as is skin, the bastard! . . .

'I wasn't made for this kinda job,' protests the trainee pimp, Eric, but softly so as not to bring the screw down on us. 'It's ruint me hands, just look at em. The caustic's eaten the skin away.'

Us, other three, keep on with our scrubbin motions. Yuh know, sprinkle the caustic on, grab old of the brush in yer right an, give it a short sweep which brung it up to that of yer neighbour. Me best mate, Chinky from Broome, a thin kid with yellow skin an stained teeth, retorts: 'What d'ya mean, we ere too.' Is words ang. What'd they mean — who knows? Ee as a soft yella voice that is yella skin fits like a glove. Broome Abo — mixed with Chinee and Japanee an who knows what else. An' ee has a yella soul too. It makes im more careful than me. Ee keeps outa blues when ee's able to, but ee came with me on that last job. . . .

'Yer right,' White Jack, a dapper con man type even in his rough shapeless prison drag, agrees. Perhaps only so ee can ear the sound of is own mellow voice. Ee fancies is self an agrees to just about anythin in is smooth con way that, if yuh don't watch out, 'll ave yuh agreein too — unless yuh it im straight in the mouth before is words get out. It was a shame what appened to im later on.

We scrub on, tossin soft words at each other. They fall short of the screw. Our lips barely move. We never look to where the words drift down. They float away, esitate an fall in front of our ears. Answers return to remind us we ain't in solitary.

'Las time I was out, I ad this ol hen waitin for me. A tough ol bird. She started out wantin to mother me, then stayed around for a length. God, she was good for a few, and more. Didn't stop till yer balls were drained dry. Just the thing for a con after a year in boob. I tell yer that, but she was built like a truck an I wanted a young'un, built like this — ' Eric's ands left off with the scrubbin an ee motioned in the air lumps of breasts, the thinness of waist, the thick swellin of ips curvin an thinnin down into legs perfect in is mind. 'An legs, man, she ad to ave em perfect, an looks, man, she ad to have em like Marilyn Monroe, yuh know — outa this world. An she ad to be (ee grinned) — perfect for the street. Well, I come across this sheila workin in Coles an she ad the lot, all that it took to keep me in cake for the rest of the year. Well, that was what I thought. Yeah, all she needed was a little trainin. Gave her that an set her to work, but, yuh know, she turned out to be no bloody good. Didn't ave the eart for it. She ad that only for me an in next to no time she was banged up. Said it was me kid, tried to lay that ole thing on me, but I wasn't avin any of it. Tol her straight just before I was picked up for somethin I didn't do. Yuh know how it is, yuh goin along swell an then they grab yuh one night for bein on the street an before you know it, yer back inside again. Only six months, but that was long enough. She met me at the bloomin gate with this little tyke who's me flamin image. What could I do?'

'Play the dada, maybe,' Jack smiled.

'Cut her up a bit, so as to teach her not to come on with the bullshit,' Ralph whispered, flashing a sadist grin at Eric.

'Not bloody likely, I'm sensitive I am. Women are money, if yuh andle em right.'

'Im an is big words,' Chinky mutters. Ee's just ad a blue with Eric an come off second best; but that appens all the time an tomorrow they'll be the best of mates again.

Ralph is taken in by Eric's phantasy dish, but ee as to add is own to it. Ee's weird this one, an scary; as sharpened a spoon, an threatens to use it on us if we annoy im. There's creeps like im even among us juveniles, an if yer show a patch of weakness, ee'll pull yuh down to is level. So now we fall quiet as is whisper pictures is sickness which threatens us as any future victim.

'It's me dream to get hold of a real fine sheila, one of those stuck-up ones. Get her all by herself and away from everything so that she can scream her head off, then cut her open a little bit at a time. You know, just take me time and do a real good job on her, take out her insides and make them her outsides. Suppose I could do that with a little practice. Christ, I can't wait to get to work. Next time it'll be nothin like this little somethin they got me for. No, it'll be bigger.'

Only sound is our scrubbin brushes, but we tough juveniles an must make some reply to this filth. 'Ow about that crazy cunt who's in for fuckin a duck,' Eric says to swerve the subject onto safer grounds.

This gives me a chance to get into the words: 'Ow'd ee get caught, that's what I'd like to know. Did is prick get caught up its arse, or what?'

'Well fuck a duck,' Chinky chimes in.

'Nother blokes in for fucking his mum,' Jack adds.

An the talk drifts from filth to filth an settles on ewes, the stockman's wife, but the rapist swings the danger back to us. Is whisper 'What about boys?' threatens us directly. Too many stories of older cons catching a juvenile an raping im as made us edgy. No one would rape Ralph, but us others. Yeah, it appened.

The screw comes out an makes an end to the talk. We scrub on, scrubbin away at our dirty fears. What was I, but a shit-scared kid, that's what we all were, except for Ralph, an ee was part of the shit that made us scared . . .

So these were me mates in jail. An what do yuh think we made ourselves into? — nuthin decent. None of us knew what decency was; none of us knew what love was either. All we knew an wanted was fuckin. A woman was nuthin but a fuck, though somethin to be leery of too. Feel em, fuck em an forget em was what we learnt, or else they got to yuh, an that was the end of it. Good college education this. Nuthin borin like from a book. Books are all cleaned up, even mine. Cleaned up with an ero whose sort of sad an withdrawn. Who might believe in nuthin, but that's not because ee was as grimy as the floor of this division, but because ee was born with a taint. Tragic ero, uh! Not bloody likely! I was just like me mates. One of em, an we stuck together all through boob, an what we got from each other never made us straight.

We even proved ourselves together. Now I can see that it was dumb, but then we all thought it was the works. Yuh see that fucking screw went on pickin on us, just went on pickin on us. Pick, pick, pickin until we ad ad enough an decided to make a stand otherwise we would be broken by the cunt. No bucket of tea though. We must've planned it durin those scrubbin sessions. That floor took months of work to clean. The grime of the prison ad sunk deep into the stone. We went on an on an over an over that stone until the ate seared us like caustic soda. We would show the bastard an our whispers grew more defiant. We knew what to do. We saved the alf loaf of bread we got for breakfast an left em in Jack's cell. Then we waited till mid-morning an when that screw was in is office. Ee was the only screw looking after the division an us juveniles. A cell on the ground floor ad bin converted into an office in which ee sat an atched is torments for us. Well, we waited till ee was in is office, then took off up to the fourth landin an into Jack's cell. We barricaded ourselves into our big moment. Not an escape though, but a confinin ourselves to a smaller space. A re'earsal for our spell of solitary confinement.

Ow many times in the past did I climb the stairs up to the landins. Impossible to calculate. Us juveniles were used as cleaners an went up and down the stairs many times each day. Now if we ad worked in one of the so-called shops, the printin or tailorin or shoe shops, then it might've bin possible to calculate. Say yuh were in for a year an worked in the printin shop. That meant that on an average you ascended an descended these stairs at least four times a day: in the mornin, for lunch an after lunch, at the end of the day, an you did this for 365 days, so this meant that you went up an down these stairs 1460 times on an average, or with other ascents an descents it might be possible to average it out to say 1900 times. I knew this guy who counted it an ee got 2010 times for a year, but for us juveniles it was up an down, down an up day after day.

Oh, I forgot to mention the floor. I don't know why. It was important, very important an a source of pain. It was made from wooden plankin an ad to be kept ighly polished. Ighly polished meant different things to different screws. Some wanted it to mirror their image, others ignored it, while others used it as an excuse to get at yuh. Just a lousy floor, but it reflected the personalities of the screws as much as it reflected our own miserable lives.

Now this is the first time in a decade that I ave eard the rattlin of the metal steps under me feet. The first time in a decade that I ear the creakin of the landin as I walk along it to the cell. But the rattlin an the creakin are old friends. I know em just as I know me first peter. Ere it is about 2·5 metres by 2·5 metres square. Just enough space to old a bed, a stool, a table bolted to the floor an a shit bucket. The walls are white-washed an in the ceilin is a single electric light bulb which is switched off at 8.30 every night. The door is metal painted black on the outside an white on the inside. About 150 centimetres from the floor is an eye-hole covered on the outside with a piece of metal which can be pushed aside. This is for the screw eye to watch us wankin, for that was the only illegal thing we done in our cell. In those days we each ad our own cell to feel the lonely ours in. We were locked in at four o'clock an let out at 8.30 in the morning for work, or to go to the exercise yard. From twelve to one we were locked in for lunch. That was life an it went on day after day, week after week, month after month, year after year — an it was in one of these cells that we decided to make our stand. This one ere. Jack's cell right on the top landin. We ad planned it like that. The screws would find it difficult to break the door down what with the landin bein so narrow, or so we thought. An ow did we lock the door, seein that the locks were on the outside with no key'oles on the inside? Well, the table could be unscrewed, an beds could be taken from other cells to make a barricade. It was easy. We all tumbled in, wedged the beds from door to end wall an waited with anticipation. It was all mateship, an Jack who ad tobacco shared out papers an flake so that we could roll up an calm our nervousness.

Strange that we never eard the screw callin to us from below. Not a sound from im. The day dragged on until lunch. It was then that we realised that the other cons weren't returnin. Then those bloody keys began janglin an doors began openin an slammin shut an janglingly locked. It went on from door to door, from bottom landin to second landin to third landin, to top landin, workin its way along to us. Suddenly, the jangle sounded outside our cell. A key was roughly inserted into the lock. Pressure was applied on the door. It opened a few inches. The beds groaned an eld. Christ, we ad forgotten to cover the eye-hole. An eye appeared before we could.

SCREW: Alright, I know that you're in there, open up, now!

RALPH: Arrh, get fucked.

The steps receded. We knew that we ad won the first round. A wave of elation overcame us. We ate our bread an waited. One thing that I forgot to describe was the window these cells ad. It was small an barred an igh in the wall. A thick metal frame held thick glass. This could be opened from the top down. Eric, I think, went to the window an opened it. Ee pressed is face against the bars an tried to look down beyond the thickness of the walls an into the exercise yards. Ee could see the far end of one of em. Convicts were in the yard. One of em glanced up an ee must've seen the face at the window. Suddenly a cheer went up. We returned it. It was good to realise that we weren't alone. It was better to know that the other cons knew what was appening an that they would be discussing us juveniles. We ad made it at last. Our stand meant somethin. So from then on, until the lunchtime was over, one or other of our faces would appear at the window to receive that ragged cheer. Of course if we stayed at the window, the cheer would die away, but if we took turns an left a couple of minutes gap between our appearances that cheer would rise up. It was great while it lasted, but screws came an the yard emptied.

It was then that the landin began creakin under the weight of more than a few eavy bodies.

SCREW: Alright, you've had your little game. Come on out.

We were silent. This was it! Our little game was over.

Suddenly the metal door thudded under a sledge-ammer. An alf a dozen blows an it swung in off its inges. Screws wrenched it aside, pushed through the gap, grabbed us an dragged us out. We made no resistance. What resistance could we ave made? It was over an, for our voluntary imprisonment in our cell, we received fourteen days solitary. . . .

Now why didn't I put that in me book, or script? I could ave tidied it up an made it more dramatic, but then Jack an Ralph an Eric don't appear in the book, though

Chinky does, an so I changed it to what I wanted personally to do to that screw, an I wanted to play the ero in my own little drama. So ere I make the record straight, while the lie continues on in the filim. The floodlights glare an the filim boys are down there. I lean over the rail an watch em set up for the shot. Ernie comes an gets ready. I notice that is curls ave bin slicked down, or rearranged into a style more in keepin with the times. The camera rolls along on a little cart in front of im. Ee is walkin along the row of cells. Is face lifts. Ee sees me an gives a grin. Well, I suppose that's okay. We did grin a lot in that cell. I can remember a grin like that on me own dial as the cons cheered our stand. It was a great feelin, a great feelin. It was as if we finally arrived.

THREE

Yuh know, the port of Fremantle is just the place for a movie. Al is ecstatic when he sees it. Per'aps it reminds him of Universal City. They ad tarted it up for a yacht race, an when the yacht race was good an lost, they kept it tarted up in the opes that it'd be a tourist's tart for ever more. Naturally, they ad been ecstatic when Al, the great Ollywood director, came to make a movie there. Good publicity, eh what? But the ol Fremantle which I knew ad disappeared. I didn't miss it that much. The main thing for me ad bin the prison an that remained snarlin over the port — at least for the time bein. Soon even that would be gone an with it whatever links I ave with this town. Maybe I won't come ere again. Still some of me memories ug this place. In me novel an now in the script, it lives on more or less a part of me. I remember a beach close to the prison, but I'm not sure where it ad been, or even if it existed. It's in the book an the script, so it must've bin real — at least in me dreams, at least in me feelins.

Still I wander across lookin for it, an finally decide that it must've bin where they moored the yachts, though before that ad bin a fishin port. Maybe before that it ad been me beach. I can't be sure, just as I can't be sure about what happened in real life an what I put in me book. Well, I'll check it out later as any beach'll do for the beach scene. It just as to feel right. But for all this, I end up at the seaside where the beach might ave bin. I go along with the others for a feed of fish an chips in the eatin place there over the water.

Only the first day of our short time, an already we ave to escape outa that dump to feel the free air on our faces. They should try bein locked up there for years and years. No escape, no fresh air. Ow do yuh think I feel after bein locked up for an eternity? I remember standin at the window of me peter, lettin this same breeze blow me emotions outa that ole. So many nights at that window glimpsin the sea, the dark waters, all that freedom of space extendin out an out without any walls to edge er in . . .

Well, we all free now, an we sit in that over-the-seas eatery scuffin up those fish an chips offa plastic plates an feelin content with avin put a good day's work be'ind us. Things've gone real smooth, even though Al ad blown is stack more'n once or twice. I avn't suffered that much in bein back in the old boob. God, I ate that place! They should raze it to the ground, not make it into some God damn museum or artsy fartsy craft centre. No way!

The fish an chips stuffed inside us, we go out along a wharf an sit on the edge lookin out over the sea. It's real nice an pleasant. Sweet Fremantle evenin with the doctor blowin cool in yer face. I'm sittin next to the Yankee director. Decide to make some conversation, see ow things are an if ee's goin to change any more of me script.

DIRECTOR: It's gonna be a sweet sweet movie. I gotta feeling for these things. I can see it. Not box office, but I'll get my money back and a little more besides. God, you guys and you gals too are natural actors. You should've been with me and seen some of the bitches and sons of bitches I've had to get a performance outa. You wouldn't believe it. . . .

SCRIPT WRITER: An yuh thinkin of changin any more of me script?

DIRECTOR: Say, listen, I've been playing this game for twenty years. I know what'll click and what won't. The one thing that the folks back home'll want to see is local colour.

VOICE: Well, yuh got that alright!

DIRECTOR: Arrh, you guys come on, kidding aside. What I mean is this is where the America's Cup race was held. It was on T.V. You just gotta jog their memory. So I'll put in a shot or two of a few yachts tacking, and then, well, there's that beach scene I shoot tomorrow. You know, there's this, what do you guys call it, a lifesavers' convention, well, something like that at, at Cottesloe. I'll shoot the scene there. Put all those muscle bodies in for the local, arrh, interest, and then go right into the scene as you wrote it. You know cut from character to carnival, back to character, to carnival and so on. Man, I can see that. It will work and it'll bring the whole thing into focus. You know the guy's been in the pen, in the slammer for over a year. He gets out all dazed and stumbles across this lady who's relaxing on the edge of the carnival. I can see it, that's what we want. All those bronze Aussie bodies. . . .

SCRIPT WRITER: Yeah, that'll be fine, real fine.

DIRECTOR: I tell you, you've gotta think visual in this art. Think visual!

SCRIPT WRITER: An what'll sell?

DIRECTOR: None of us are in it for the art, guy!

SCRIPT WRITER (sings): The best things in life are free./Yuh can give em to the birds an bees./I want money, that's what I want.

KEVIN: Talkin of beaches, up in Broome, they ave this wide beach, Cable Beach, goes on for miles. We fish off it. I was up there not so long ago an was with these old geezers, an I eard this story, real Aboriginal story this one, so yuh better listen, Al!

DIRECTOR: Say, you mean just like the story in the script, that's local colour, local colour — too bad it got in the way of the story line.

KEVIN: Yeah, this one's local colour alright, though it ain't got nothin to do with the script. Bout Monkey an

Turtle. Two brothers — what we call bublies. Well, these two bublies go out together for bush tucker. They go out for bush tucker an come across this fruit tree. You know, Australian tree with fruit on it just like a plum. An Monkey ee climbs that tree an begins eatin that fruit. Ee stuffs em fruits into is mouth an spits out the stones. They go plop plop plop all around poor Turtle. Ee wants some too. Ee calls: 'Ey, bubly, come on, ow bout me?' No answer. That greedy monkey, ee keeps on gutsin is self, maybe now an then ee throws down a green one for is brother. Turtle, ee calls again: 'Send me down some, eh!' Ee's startin to get wild at that monkey. Ee goin to fix im. Ee looks about, sees sharp stones layin on the ground. Ee gets em. Puts em all around the foot of that tree. Well, that monkey goes on gutsin is self, an is belly gets out like this. At last ee finish. Ee so full that ee just slides down the tree trunk an right onto those sharp stones. Ee leaps up. Now ee's wild too.

'For that, I'm goin to kill yuh,' ee shouts.

'Yeah, you kill me!' An Turtle picks up is spear. Ee dances up an down an shouts: 'Yeah, kill me, kill me!'

Monkey, ee looks at that wild Turtle, an ee says: 'No, spearin'll be too easy, I'll burn yuh alive.'

Turtle grabs up chunks of wood an flings them at Monkey while shoutin: 'Yeah, wood here, go on make a fire an chuck me in it.'

'No, that too good for yuh. I know what I'll do, I'll throw yuh into the sea.'

'No, bubly, no, no!'

'Yeah, chuck yuh in the sea.'

Ee leaps on Turtle, swings im around an out into the sea.

Turtle lands with a great splash. Ee goes under. Ee finds that ee can swim with is flappers. Ee takes a good look around an says to is self: 'Ey, looks like a nice place ere, all those pretty corals an white sand, an arrh — just ad a nice feed of jellyfish — arrh, real nice.'

In the meantime old Monkey is sorry for what ee's

done, an ee calls out: 'Ey, bubly, bubly, come back, I didn't mean to do it.'

'Not on yer life. This place is too good. Goin to check it all out. See yuh when I get back.'

An Turtle, ee swims away. . . .

That's ow they tell it up Broome way, an they say that's the reason why Turtle is in the sea an Monkey is up in a tree — scared of gettin his feet cut if ee comes down. One thing though, yuh know, puzzles me, there ain't no monkeys up Broome way, monkeys don't belong to Australia.

'Dunno bout that,' I say to Kevin as I get to me feet an wander along the wharf to where the girls are sittin. At least I know who'll be gettin all of the plums outa the filim, an' it won't be us, but some foreign ape.

So me bitterness as returned. I feel like goin to the pub to sink a few, or more, but as I pass the girls, one calls out to me and I see that Jinda Cole is there. She arrived just this afternoon an is to play Denise in the filim. Naturally she is beautiful with a fine dancer's body an long black hair streaked with gold, but she affects some sort of Grace Jones butch image which puts me off. I like me women tender an Koori-soft in the mind so that they are nice to be with, so that they are nice to ear with that sweet Koori softness of voice like meltin butter, but Jinda as one of those educated voices that puts me on guard straight way. Maybe it's because she's from Sydney an that town breeds em ard. I dunno, but she isn't like Denise. she was one yuh could relax with. Yeah, at least in me dreams. Dunno bout Jinda playin er. Some'ow the country is gone from er; some'ow that got lost in Sydney. I sit with er an look over the waters, thinkin of Denise, romantic wet dream, an when Jinda mentions that she is a little nervous bout playin er, I begin talkin bout Denise, but not really cause I'm funnin, an me words are directed at that lush-bodied girl, at that Renee. Every now an again I look outa the corner of me eye to see ow she's takin it.

'I was real naive then,' I begin. Yuh know, seventeen an never bin kissed. Didn't believe in love either, or any of that jive. None of us did. Them were the days you ad to be cool, an yuh didn't let on what yuh were feelin, or thinkin. It came natural after that orphanage. Maybe I was lonely as ell, what with gettin outa that ome an tryin to make me way without knowin me way. Started angin out at that milk-bar. Then one day Denise came into the place. She was really somethin, yuh know, tall and dark like black fire, with almond brown eyes which really smouldered. Never believed before that eyes could smoulder, but ers did. An she ad this black air to which she did things, pilin it an pullin it to this side or the other in a way none of the other girls that ung around the place could match.'

I flash a glance at the lush-bodied girl, that Renee. She is all ears so I continue me invention. Anyway she ad bin me dream doll.

'She ad a perfect nose, ands that should've bin strokin an instrument, an the kind of legs an thighs yuh only see in girly magazines, or in filims. She was first class, a real dreamboat.

'That time, that special time when she turned up, she walked through the door an the ole place died. I can see her still. She came in the door an stopped just inside. The light made an alo around er body dressed in jeans an sweat shirt — but it was the way she wore em that mattered. I wanted to make er mine right then, but she came in with some bloke, who I soon found out couldn't take squeezin without runnin. Well, that was later; this time I just watched as she went to a table. She didn't walk, she sorta glided. "That's grace" I said to meself. An she didn't throw erself down into a chair, if yuh get me meanin, but sat. I watched as she leaned over a cup of coffee. The perfect cones of er breasts thrust down as she rested er perfect chin in the perfect taperin of er long fingers. A gold charm bracelet dangled bout one smooth delicate brown wrist.

'Yuh know, I was gaga over this bird — an when she kept on comin in, I leant on er boyfriend, an before I knew it I was in an ee was out. But yuh know one thing, the thing that got me ooked was that yuh could never be sure of er. Other girls wanted to be owned. They were appy to be known as Billy's girl, or Tommy's girl an so on, but Denise was just Denise. Anyway, that didn't create problems, I didn't want to be known as Denise's bloke anyway, an so it kept all casual. Maybe it should've bin different, but she liked me, was a friend, I could count on er, an that was enough for both of us, maybe? That bloody "cool" sure fucked up feelin. Anyway she was a friend an more than a friend, an I ad to downplay the miracle of just bein with er.

'Yuh know, when I was with er things changed. Say I'm goin along a street an doing the usual thing of walkin. One foot placed before t'other, then the back foot swung past on its leg to it the pavement in front. Yuh know, just walkin along the street, perhaps listenin to the sounds of me shoes, perhaps not, for I wore what was called brothel creepers an sorta bounced silently along on thick rubber soles. Still, what I'm gettin at is that walkin is automatic, just one of those things. It wasn't that way with Denise — when she went along the street, magic flowed along with er. Dunno what it was, yuh ad to see er to believe it. She wasn't like some sorta machine. She was like a priest at mass. Yuh know, all those gestures an movements all meanin somethin, an all woven into some sorta ritual or dance; but not like a dance — dancin is too obvious. Maybe it was like she was carrying some sorta secret message; it was as if somethin was livin which ad no right to be livin. She was all those old pop songs come together in one moment of magic . . .'

I look round at em, look at their faces. Women love romance, love feelin that us men appreciate em for more than they are worth. Still, in a way, all of em are carryin secret messages. I decide to bring em down a little, especially that one with the lush body an brown eyes filled with romantic lust.

'An guess what, yuh know I can't even remember anything bout the first time I fucked her. It was a big bore,
zilch, zero.' (I look into Renee's large brown eyes.) 'Yuh
know ow it is with the terrific lookers, they to be seen, not
to be fucked.' (That got to er, but I go on.) 'Yuh know, it
wasn't er first time, but she was as bad as a virgin. Maybe
it was because she did it sometimes for money an it ad
become just a job to be done? Just one of those things
yuh ad to be cool about. I dunno?'

Jinda wisely nods an says that she knows ow it is. This
puts me off me story. Maybe she as got somethin inside er
after all? But me story is not for er, but for t'other. I
decide to finish it off as I started it, romantic, real
Barbara Cartland stuff. I ain't a writer for nuthin, yuh
know. Then I ave got carried away with me words an ave
to give me character some sorta decent ending.

'Yuh know, I remember one day, ow it rained an
rained an we went out walkin, strollin in the rain, smilin
an dry in er magic. Smilin, cryin day. I remember that
day, an the sudden cry of Denise callin to me from across
the road, an she runnin across to me with er magic
streamin about an be'ind an in front in that appy run, in
that appy rain, from that appy face, from that appy body.
I remember all that, that magic street, that magic rain; an
us walkin in that rain, an she ran from me takin the
magic with er. I got wet in that rain, caught a cold an
then other things appened.' I scowl an go silent. Got
carried away then. Recover an say: 'Anyway, it's better in
the script an you'll ave read it. She was a friend an more
than a friend.'

Renee begins to say somethin, but I walk away to the
very edge of the wharf an look over. A paper cup is floatin
there, bobbin an bobbin, up an down, up an down.
Suddenly, somethin soft pushes into me back an I find
meself fallin an fallin towards that paper cup. I go under
with a gasp an surface to laughter. I don't find it very
funny. Could get wild, could get real mad, but the water
is cold an, unlike Turtle, I don't find coral growin in the
current pushin up from the south. In fact, it's too cold to

feel wild about anythin, an so I grin up at em an swim over to a metal ladder an climb up with all romance washed outa me soul. It ad bin fun yarnin to em an re-inventin a friend from the past, but she was more like me mum an looked after me.

Yeah, I remember that time I cut me foot on a piece of glass idden in the grass. I looked at the blueness beneath the flesh an panicked. 'Mum, mum,' me child's voice cried—and mum was there with comfort an a piece of cobweb to stop the blood. Denise was like that. No magic, just easin the urt. I ope that sorta feelin comes through in the movie, but I look at Jinda smilin at me discomfort an know me friend is gone for ever. Denise will be like Jinda, an Jinda is more like the Denise of me imagination than the Denise of me life. What can I do, but say 'fuck it', an let the cameras roll. Life is only dreams an feelins. Cut!

FOUR

Beach. Afternoon.

The beach. Lifesaving carnival is in progress. Life-savers marching and engaging in lifesaving exercises.

Ernie stands watching. He carries his jacket over his shoulder, a finger serving as a hook. He shrugs and moves off, skirting the activity.

A girl is stretched out on the sand apparently sleep-ing. She wears a white one-piece bathing suit. A large pair of sunglasses hide her eyes and most of her upper face.

Ernie pulls off his tie. He unbuttons his shirt and takes it off. He flops down on the sand near, but not too near the girl. He sits and glances at the lifesavers, then at the girl. He shrugs.

Ernie: *Ullo!*

The girl does not reply, or move. Perhaps she is asleep and has not heard him.

Ernie: *Like you dead, or in a yogi trance, or somethin like that?*

The girl slowly moves. She raises herself on an elbow. Her masked face turns towards him.

Ernie: *Ullo!*

The girl stares towards him, or through him, perhaps at a lifesaving boat which is rushing through the surf.

June: *Do I know you?*

Ernie looks at her with an expression defying her to know him, or not to . . .

Ernie: *Maybe the answer is 'yes', maybe the answer is 'no', maybe the answer is — do I know you? Nice day for the beach, isn't it?*

He turns his head and stares at the boat being pulled up onto the beach. The girl is seen in the background raised on one elbow.

Ernie: *Nice day for a loaf, isn't it? Just lie back and take it easy, not a care in sight.*
June: *Yes, you lie back — and then some idiot comes along . . .*
Ernie: *Yeah, someone always comes along, but then sometimes nobody comes along and that's worse, far worse!*
June: *Is it?*
Ernie: *Take me word for it. . . .*

The girl glances at her wrist watch. She stretches, sits up and begins flicking sand off her legs with her towel. Ernie stares at her legs, again with the defiant expression on his face.

Ernie: *Yeah, I know people can be a drag, but then I get sick and tired of talkin to meself. It's a bit like — oh, forget it. . . .*

The girl is half smiling as if ready to accept his challenge.

June: *Yes, I know what you mean, but then I do like getting off by myself too. You might even see it as a bad habit, but I'm like that.*

Ernie's face turns mean.

Ernie: *I know just the place for you. Try a prison cell an just see ow you like gettin off by yerself.*

The girl begins brushing the sand off her legs again. It is a deliberate slow action—a sensual action. Something is going on between them beyond their words.

Ernie: *So now you've ad yer bad experience for the day. You can run on ome and tell 'em ow yuh were molested almost by a jailbird whose just bin released. Guess, it's not yer lucky day.*
June: *Oh, great, just great. . . .*

She exaggerates a yawn, one hand covering her mouth.

June: *A real live jailbird. I've always wanted to be molested by one. How long were you in for? Two days for jay walking?*

Ernie's face shows that he is anxious to make an impression.

Ernie: *Eighteen lousy months for somethin I didn't do. Didn't deserve to serve a day. Nah, they could've got me for somethin better than robbin a stupid shop for a couple of coins.*

The girl watches him. She does not find him a threat.

June: *I have heard that your sort always go to jail for not doing anything.*
Ernie: *Next time, it'll be different. . . .*
June: *You just got out, today I take it, and perhaps I'm*

*the first person you've spoken to, and here you are
discussing the next time. I thought the prison system
was geared towards rehabilitation? . . .*
Ernie: *Rehabilitation, that's a joke. It's a college; yuh
go there to learn not to get caught.*

The girl is interested in the conversation. It is her first
encounter with a criminal, and she is studying soci-
ology at the university.

June: *Well, I suppose you can become used to anything in time. Anyway, what do people do in prison
these days? I suppose that breaking rocks is of the
past? . . .*

Ernie stares past her at the lifesavers parading. He
looks around at the long length of beach, at the open
sky and the ocean, then at the girl.

Ernie: *Yuh never get used to that place, never! An what
do we do in there? Eat, sleep, shit, swap yarns, read
books — cut out pictures of good-looking sorts from
magazines. Stick em on the walls, stare at em at night,
wait for the screws to come along an rip em off the
walls. Sometimes climb up on the bed an look through
the bars at the ocean an wish to sit on a beach like this
with one of those girls. Yuh know, just doin all those
dumb things which makes the time drag.*

The girl observes him dispassionately.

June: *Doesn't sound like much of a life. What sort of
books did you read in there?*
Ernie: *A lot of em yuh wouldn't even look at, but then
I got sick of readin westerns an things like that. I ad to
clean the library out once, an saw that they ad this
encyclopaedia, about twenty or so volumes. I used to
get that. Started from A an read me way through it.*

*Almost made it to the end too, but me time ran out.
Maybe I'll finish it next time I'm in.*
June: *God, you're the first person I've met who's read
an encyclopaedia.*
Ernie: *It took some readin, an time too. Yuh know,
they put out the lights at alf past eight, but I got a
bloke to make me up a little kerosene lamp, just a little
bottle with a ole in the lid an a bit of cloth pushed
through. Yuh pull the blankets over yer ead so that the
screws can't see the light, then yuh can read for most of
the night. Ad to swap me tobacco ration for the kero,
but it was worth it.*
June: *What sort of education did you have before you
decided to broaden your knowledge?*
Ernie: *Primary school. Ad to go, I was in one of those
omes an yuh couldn't get outa it. I was one of the
smart ones, didn't get bashed much —*
June: *Oh . . .*
Ernie: *Yeah, OH! more like OUCH! When I got outa
that place that was the end of it. Then I got a real
education. In the Noongar camps, learnt there who
were me friends, an a lot else besides.*
June: *Noongar?*
Ernie: *Aborigine to you.*

He stares out to sea. The girl's interested face is in the
background. She stares at him hard.

June: *Arrh, so that explains it.*
Ernie: *Explains what?*
June: *The tan.*
Ernie: *Yeah, don't have to lie all day on the beach just
to go brown. It's me birthright. Even jail couldn't
remove it.*

The girl's eyes move away from Ernie. A muscular
blond lifesaver strolls past. Her eyes follow him. Ernie
twists his mouth.

June: *But you're not a full blood?*
Ernie: *What does it matter?*

Her eyes fasten on him again.

Ernie: *Me mum was; me dad wasn't. Some Watjela, white bloke who went diggin for gold an struck black gold. Good luck for im, tough luck for mum. Ee died an left her with nuthin, but some kids like me. She didn't ave those for long either. They took us away to omes an left er with nuthin but tears.*

The girl removes her sunglasses. Her eyes are concerned, then she glances at her watch, gives a start, and smiles.

June: *Gosh, is that the time? Well, well, it's been nice meeting you, but I've got to rush.*

Ernie watches the back of the lifesaver in the distance. The man turns and begins to sprint towards them. He tears past, his churning feet spraying sand over Ernie. He flinches.

Ernie: *Yeah, yuh gotta run alright, after im!*

The girl starts indignantly.

June: *Oh come on — anyway why don't you follow his example? Get into a pair of togs and get into the sea instead of watching it.*

Ernie deliberately gets to his feet and begins stripping down to his underpants. The girl eyes his long thin legs, his narrow hips and broad shoulders. He stands consciously posing. He flashes a suddenly carefree smile down at her.

Ernie: *Well, see yuh, I'm off to ave a dip.*
June: *Hey, wait on, we can't leave it like this? . . .*
Ernie: *Why not, we ad a nice little yarn didn't we?*
June: *We might continue some other time? . . .*
Ernie: *Maybe?*
June: *I go to the university. Why don't you meet me there tomorrow, say in the afternoon, in the Coffee Shoppe. I'll be there about two. By the way, what's your name, mine's June.*
Ernie: *June, just like in the month?*
June: *Yes.*
Ernie: *Well, see yuh June, that water looks good.*

He flashes again the carefree grin and dashes into the surf. . . .

DIRECTOR: Cut, cut! Ernie that last bit made the scene. Great acting, man!

I dunno about that. In fact I don't even know if I wanted it played like that. Anyway yuh never can tell ow it'll turn out when they get through with it. It might be like this an then again it mightn't. I ain't got any control over it — cept maybe the way Ernie's playin me character. In the script there ain't no carefree smile. I'm sure of that. After all the poor bastard's just got outa boob, an this is is first attempt to regain the land of the livin, so as to speak. The director must've fucked it up. Told Ernie to play the sweet beguilin sexy young'un for the American audience. 'They like balls and footy and booze and speed. Why, they're just like us.' Yuh know ow they think! Well, nuthin to do, but go along with it. Wait for the finished product, an ope for the best. Anyway, I've signed away me rights, an ave to put up with it. . . .

Most of the rest of the cast are on the beach for a swim an do what people do on the beach. Renee, the girl is there in a one-piece bathing suit that makes me move closer for a close-up. She smiles at me as I come near an says: 'Well, that scene went really well. Kylie is really beautiful, isn't she?'

'Yuh know,' I say to er, 'she's all that I ate. Blonde air, blue eyes, long legs, narrow waist, nice breasts. Yuh name it an she as it all along with that educated accent. Christ, she's June alright, an I bet she'd ask the same questions too to im!'

Renee's smile leaves er face. She stares at me, then replies: 'I don't know about that. I would think that she's all that you should love.'

I don't know ow to answer er. Am saved when Ernie tears up scatterin water over us an flashin that carefree smile I'm beginnin to ate. I watch as er face lights up, an she dismisses me with er luscious back. It seems she's in love with im, but I ear tell there's another woman in Sydney she don't know about. That's ow it is these days, but then it's no business of mine, though it might make things a little easier in the long run. Just ave to ang in there, an wait for it, bradda. That's ow it should be. There's always the right time for things.

The sea an the sand an the sun are so nice that I decide to follow Ernie's example an strip off an go in for a dip. Put on a pair of underpants this morning just for it. I strip off, an let me body ave a go at that sun an sea an sand. This is ow it should be. I see Ernie runnin into the surf. Ee as a Koori body. A unter's body. Long thin legs, deep chest, an not much weight around the waist — yet! I've got a bit, not that much though. Try to keep meself in some sort of shape. A beer belly perched on spindly legs urts me racial pride. Yuh know, black is beautiful! I flash a grin an run into the surf. I dive quickly, giving a gasp as the cold of the water goosepimples me body. Soon get used to it, an I swim out towards the orizon while thinkin, thinkin of Ernie an what ee's doin to me character, to me. I get an idea. I'll get im off to one side tonight an ave a little talk with im. Ee ain't never bin in jail, doesn't know what it's like, so ow can ee play me. Yeah, ow can ee? Ee needs a little taste of what's it's like bein scared an defiant both at the one time. Ee's got to get it right!

I smile, turn on me back an float. Green sea, blue sky, white sand — what more do yuh need? I turn an swim back, feelin better than I've felt all week. Wade back onto the beach an find meself confrontin the brown trickster face of Kev. 'Ow do yuh think it's goin?' I ask im.

KEVIN: Okay, bubly, Al knows is stuff.

'Yeah, but ee keeps changin things.'

KEVIN: Ee is a Watjela.

'Yeah, but ee could try an be more Aboriginal.'

KEVIN: That'll take some doin.

We walk off along the sand, an I grin an say: 'Ey, yuh know that Jacky yarn yuh told. I know another one. It follows on from it. Yuh know, they get Jacky to enter that lift. Ee doesn't want to. Ee thinks that ee'll change, but we tell im that ee won't. At last we all get into it an press the button an go up to another floor. The doors open, an ee looks out an says: "Other people get into this little room, door closes, then door opens an they different. We get into this room, door closes an then door opens an — Ey, new world!"'

We laugh an after I tell Kev that this movie business is a different world for me.

'Yeah,' ee answers, 'it's new for all of us, bubly, all new, another mob altogether this lot is. Some good-lookin sheilas amongst em though.'

'Yeah, know what yuh mean,' I agree thinkin of Renee an er body, an er voice, an nuthin at all as I come across Kylie an decide to talk. What ad Renee said: She's all that I should love? Maybe, but maybe not — don't feel that she's me type. But she's a good sort. Nuthin racist, or stand-offish in er at all. Still it's the accent that puts me off. People that talk like she does are snobs an only interested in themselves, or they are like June, the character in me book, who from the top of the mountain extends an elpin and to the poor bloody blacks. Well, sod the lot of em, or maybe not? Nuthin wrong with this girl in front of me. Uman bein an all that.

FIVE

That night we're to ave a few drinks in the part which as bin made over into a set for the loft party which, Al says, will be shot after the coffee shop scene. Ee seems to keep to some sorta system, though I can't figure it out. It messes up me time direction somethin awful doin scenes outa context. Anyway, the old prison chapel as bin done over into a loft. The whitewashed walls an the sloped roof without a ceilin to ide the rafters make it look like the real thing. I put in me money for Kev to go an get a couple of cartons of cans. Ee's soon back, an we get stuck into em. To tell the truth, I still feel that prison atmosphere pressin in on me, though not as eavy as before. I've got me plan all ready for Ernie. Ee's puttin away a few. Good! Need im a little charged. I take im another can an watch as ee pops the top. Renee is with im, an as always she looks lovely. I smile at er, then tell er that this place as bin the prison chapel.

She wants to ear more, but I'm rememberin this place. I go an get another can to dampen down the feelins. We came ere to fill in Sunday. Of course yuh ran the risk of bein brainwashed, an there were some who were. Me mate, Chinky was one of em, though only on the inside. Ee never carried it over into the outside where it might ave done im some good. A memory pops into me mind. It makes me grin. They usedta bring in outsiders sometimes for some sorta communion of the faithful. Once this was a group of women, nice young'uns, fresh an innocent lookin. Dunno why this Christian mob done it, but they did. Just imagine all those cons with their tongues angin out. We began an ymn, an their sweet voices rose to the eavens while ours scraped along the floor, an tried to inch up their skirts. . . . I giggle over what appened durin that service. It's too good to keep to meself. I look around for Kev. Ee's standin with Al. I go an break into their conversation.

'Yuh know,' I say, 'this was the chapel. I came along ere one Sunday to mingle, for the priest was bringin along some of is female congregation to keep our spirits up an our lust flowin. Well, we got into the ymn singin, an towards the end of one, maybe it was 'Rock of Ages', I felt this fart buildin up. It built up an built up. Tried to old it in. No use, an just as the ymn came to an end out it came in a long drawn out squeal. Yuh oughta eard it. I kept me face straight, some of the other cons flashed grins, an those sheilas, they didn't know what to do. Eeeeeeeeeeeeh! The priest maintained is cool though, I give you that. Ee carried on as if nuthin ad appened to spoil the spirituality of it all. But that fart made the service for us. It was so funny, bro. Yuh would've split yer sides laughin if yuh ad bin there.'

They both laugh, an me story sets Kev off. 'Yuh know,' ee begins, 'we were at a conference once, an there was this middle-aged American woman there. We get some queer'uns at our conferences an she was one of em. Well, we were avin a few drinks, just like we are now, after an ard day of tryin to get things together, an she's there among us. We knew what she wanted soon enough. Yuh know, black cock. She started comin on eavy with us. We soon got the drift where er mind was at, an led er on. We just weren't interested. We've learnt to be careful. Yuh know, they often out to sabotage our conferences. There was one where there was a white woman askin for it, an when she got it, she screamed rape. Well, we were all quartered in a college an were finishin our drinks after the bar ad closed. Then we made for our rooms. She

tagged along with the remark: "Ope I don't get raped."
We all went to me room for a yarn an she followed us in.
After a while she said: "Ope you boys got your condoms
ready?" Well, we weren't goin to be in anythin like that,
an I replied for all of us: "Yeah, I have, but one of me
mates can go first." Then we gammoned er, we all began
sayin: "No, yuh first; me last, me last; no, yuh first, me
last." She soon got the message an left. Only way to andle
it, yuh know.'

Clarissa as eard the last part of the story an gets upset.
She mutters 'sexist', but no one takes er up on it, an Al
begins a story about ow, when a lot of American Jewish
people began travelling to Israel, the Israeli airline, El
Al, instructed its crew members to learn Yiddish, which
is the language American Jews speak, an ee tells us ow on
one trip, the pilot announced after take-off.

'Shalom, ladies and gentlemen and welcome to El Al
airlines. This is your pilot, Avi Goldberg, wishing you a
happy, restful trip, which we certainly expect you to
have, God willing. And if by some remote chance we do
run into trouble — God forbid — do not panic, keep calm.
Your lifebelt is under your seat, and if you must put it on,
wear it in good health.'

We all laugh politely, though we don't exactly get the
point. Then Kev begins an airplane story, an I escape
back to Ernie who's quite merry, an in keepin with the
theme is singin a two word song: 'Armen, well, armen,
well armen' — over an over again.

'You wanta get some cigarettes,' I ask im when ee
finally gives it away. We go off together. Is girl flashes a
smile, but she's deep in conversation with the blonde an
doesn't follow after. That's good, for I want Ernie by is
self.

We go out to the front of the prison an ead towards the
gates. They're open, of course, they never goin to be
closed on men again, at least I ope so. Still can't suppress
a feelin of the walls closin in on me as I walk across the
narrow yard.

'Yuh know,' I tell Ernie. 'Can't get used to bein in this

place. It still gets to me. Still can feel their eyes on me. See those watch towers up there. They were manned twenty-fours a day with screws with rifles. They seemed always to be watchin me. I even saw their eyes in me dreams, an then at night if they saw yer face in the window, they yelled for yuh to get down, or counted the window, an rang through to the division screws, the ones on duty inside, an before yuh knew it there was this eye at the peep-ole an yuh were on a charge. They wore sand-shoes at night, so that they could creep along an perve on yuh. Bastards! God, I dream about those eyes, wake up sweatin even now.'

I take a pull on me can an Ernie follows suit. Ee's not sayin much. Perhaps ee's too busy keepin is mind on is legs which seem to lurch im from one side to the other. I ease im through the gate an we stand lookin into the town. The narrow approach road sweeps down, an there is a low wall on either side with a drop. No detours allowed, it is either straight away or straight in.

'Yuh know,' I say to im, as we stagger down to where I remember a shop used to be. It is long gone an we continue on into town. It is just after ten an everything is closed. Well, the cigarettes was only an excuse. We walk through the empty streets, an I begin again: 'Yuh know, yer okay in the picture, but yuh gotta put more eart in it. Yuh gotta feel em eyes on yuh; yuh gotta wake up in the mornin drippin wet from the sweat of yer nightmares. It's gotta be like that, yuh know, paranoia! Them bastards are standin over yuh; one false move an it's into solitary with yuh; two false moves an they'll put the boot into yuh; three false moves an yer good as dead. Yuh get me!'

Ee stops an slowly nods is ead as ee mutters: 'Yeah, I get yuh.'

I know ee doesn't, but I'm ere to fix that. I finish off me can of beer an get im to finish off is. We go into a pub which is just about to close an get two stubbies. That'll be enough. We go around the block an begin to circle back to the prison. I stop an undo the top of the stubby an take a long pull. The beer is icy cold an goes down smoothly. No one except us is on the street. I look at the lighted windows of the shops at our side, then tell im: 'Goin to do a little thing for the folks to remember us. Yuh know, when they ad the yacht race ere, they tried to keep the Aborigines outa town. We aven't forgotten that!'

I tug out the spray can of black paint I bought that afternoon, an as he watches, I spray along the shop windows:

WHITES YOU MURDER US

I was goin to add BLACKS, but the can runs out of paint. Angrily, I fling it at a shop window. It bounces off an into the gutter. Suddenly, Ernie flings is stubby at a window. It too bounces off, but its the pavement an shatters.

'That's ow yuh end up inside,' I tell im, 'for doin somethin stupid like that.'

Instant recognition its im in the face. Ee's just a kid on top of the world an with no desire to play a rebel except in the movies. Is drunkeness don't protect im from realisin what ee's done, but it inders is thought processes as the blue light of a police car turns the corner an speeds towards us. Now we are in the shit, an 'Officer, I ain't done nuthin' won't mean a thing — what with the drippin paint, the empty spray can, the smashed stubby, the one still in me hand, an the colour of our skins. We're fucked, mate! Naw, never, bradda!

'Come on, down this lane, too narrow for the pigs to come after us in the car.'

We scoot down the lane just like in the movies, but this is for real, as real as that time when I was at that store.

As I run the whole thing flashes into me mind. The ol Olden car pullin up in front of a pair of five foot igh gates covered with wire mesh an chained together in the middle with a big padlock shinin in the light of me torch. Be'ind it bulk rows an eaps of petrol drums. Chinky is with me. Ee follows me over the gates. They rattle loudly, as loudly as the trash can which I stumble over an send rollin away. It brings me outa me memories. 'Right, bro,' I tell Ernie. 'I betcha anything that the pigs are drivin aroun to cut us off at the end of the lane. So we'll just double back an lose em.' Ee as enough sense to listen to me. That time, when I shot the cop, Chinky panicked an ran into the town an was caught. I went into the bush. It didn't matter though. I was caught later, too, but this time we ain't goin to be caught. Not on yer life, mate!

The end of the lane is clear as I knew it would be. We run past the shops an slow down as we near the front of the prison. We walk up, or rather stagger as the grog returns to aunt us. It's nice an quiet as we stumble our way to the prison ospital where we're puttin up.

I know Ernie as bin real scared by what we done, then so ave I. It drags me away from sleep, then it comes an I wake screamin an calling for me mum. Ad a stupid dream. Old dream, but mixed up. About a cat that was flyin, flyin igh, an a crow came dashin down an pecked out its eyes. Then, it was real funny, I came awake in that dream, an I was a kid again an in that little ouse we used to live in. I got outa me bed an went to mum, but it wasn't er. It was Clarissa, an I begged to get into bed with er. I ad bin frightened by the same dream, then it all changed again. I was grown up, not old, but about sixteen an I was lyin in a bed, an they came for me. I was just lyin there, an these two demons, detectives, yuh know, they came in an one said: 'Well, well, here he is just like the last time.'

And the other replied: 'Wakey, wakey, yuh got a little trip ter make.' Ee puts out an and an I try to throw it off. Start to struggle, though knowin it'll do no good, but I won't give in. Is and presses down on me chest like a ton of bricks. I start to suffocate — an it's then that I scream an wake up to find it day an the others gettin ready for the shootin. Thank God, the last scene'll soon be shot in this place. I've ad enough of it. Just the loft party, an after that, or maybe it's before, I dunno, we'll be shootin the Coffee Ouse scene at the university an then it's all over bar the country. God, I'll be glad to get out into the bush.

I lay there tryin to get some sanity back into me life. I ope Ernie didn't take it all that seriously last night. I adn't expected a cop car to come cruisin along. Still, it wasn't such a big thing, an we would've got off with a fine seein that we workin in a movie an all that.

Finally, I drag meself up for a shower. The ospital is the best part of the prison, but still there is that jail smell bout it that makes me uneasy. I don't see why we couldn't ave stayed in a otel anyway, but Al was all for us sleepin in the jail to soak up the atmosphere an all that. I betcha that ee's already got the publicity prepared. They've bin takin stills of us in ere. It'll be a nice touch. Yeah, great, but not for me. I go into the shower stall an suddenly it's all there, either outa the past, or outa the novel, or outa the script. I don't know any more. All I know is that the feelins there. God, I'll be glad to get out. . . .

But apprehension, yeah that's it, lurks. Under that prison shower, I feel scared, not of the inside, but of the outside. I look across at Chinky who's gettin out at the same time as me, an wonder if ee too feels scared. I soap me body an that apprehension leaves as suddenly as it it. Deep down, I'm glad that it's over. Ow I ate those screws always lookin, always lookin at yuh. Even on this last day they lookin, lookin as I soap me body an try to clean it of the prison stink — as I dry it, tryin to wipe off the prison stink. Then we are marched with towels around us into another room where our civvy suits ang. I fancy meself as a good dresser, an ate gettin into the blue serge suit made in the tailorin shop. Then us mob also as our own air style, but a bastard of a screw as got rid of that. I dress meself an look in the mirror an see lookin back at me a jailbird. I don't like it one bit, an it brings back me apprehension. First thing, I'll do when I get out will be to look up a mate to borrow some decent gear, then, then what? — mix with the old mob again, an see Denise, an do the thing we bin talkin about for years in ere, that is fuck er! I like Denise, I mean I liked er. Met er in that dance place called The Snakepit. It played our kind of music an that was important then.

The all was dark an sweaty an ow I liked it. Just the place for me to pose in. This cat was cool, man! I stood at the side of the dance floor feelin good an just right. Spot on! Me air was long an slick with grease. I ad on black jeans, black shirt, a black vinyl jacket an pointy-toed black shoes. I was the cat's eyes, an me face eld that supercilious look cats old. I smile a cat's smile an slowly pull out a cigarette an light it. The smoke spirals up an smarts me eyes, makin em slit. That's ow I like em to be. Denise comes over to me. God, this is just a fuckin daydream. Denise is just Jinda. All city ard, though still more a kid than a woman. I watch the smoke of me fag.

JINDA: This place is a bit slow?

I answer: 'What place ain't?'

JINDA: It's steamin hot in here, and they still can dance.

I reply: 'Watched a black cat once. On eat. It went roun an roun just like em, then dropped down dead — crazy!'

JINDA: Crazy!

Er forehead is damp with sweat an an ank of air angs listlessly over an eye. She's restless. Er eyes flicker round the all.

'Want some air?'

JINDA: Yeah, why not, the joint's dead tonight.

We wander outa the all an towards the bank of the Swan River which is a block away. Perth is small. She stumbles when she reaches the grass an me and goes out to steady her. I find she is leanin against me, an I kiss her. Don't know much about kissin, but what can yuh expect? Then I touch er breast. Real kicks, but I'm scared to go on. The orphanage never told me about girls an what to do with em. So we sit an just talk. I skite a bit.

'Got some dough yesterday, bought some new threads, yuh like em?'

JINDA: Alright, you buy em at that new shop that just opened?

'Yeah.'

JINDA: Must've cost a bit?

'A bit, but then that poor box ad enough in it. Weak lock too.'

JINDA: You didn't rob a poor box?!

'Yeah, I'm poor, ain't I?'

JINDA: You must've been scared, you know, God. . . .

'Nah, ain't no God, I know, I dared im to stop me.'

JINDA: Arrh, you're silly sometimes, plain silly.

'Silly, for yuh, doll.' . . .

Big deal, huh? No wonder, I wasn't so wrapt in gettin out. I didn't know much before I went inside. It was only there I learnt about sheilas like Denise an ow I could've ad er for the takin. An I did too later, but still I can't remember er face now. Jinda took care of that, just as Clarissa's taken care of me mum's face. Now nothing is real except the book, an the script an the actors playin in the filim. Some'ow, it seems that that's all I've got of me past. They there to make me past real for me an they gotta do it right. That was the reason why we did that stupid thing last night. Yuh know, give Ernie some experience so that ee can play me right.

The cameras are ready to roll, an there is Ernie all dressed up in a blue serge suit, but ee still as air. Ee looks different this mornin, more wary, an the carefree smile of is doesn't flash at all. Not even once. Ee glances at me an is eyes slide away. I watch as ee gets ready to play out the release scene. Ee stands in front of the main prison gates surrounded by cameras. It is then that two police constables come towards the group. Al is all ready for a take, but they barge in an spoil the set-up. They look around at us, their eyes settlin on our dark faces. They turn from us an to Al, who as a white man must be in charge. They march to im an begin:

'Seems like a bit of vagrancy was committed last night. A couple of your boys were seen running away from the scene of the crime. We've come to make a few inquiries, if you don't mind!'

AL: Mind? Mind? Of course I mind! I've rented this

place for a thousand dollars a day, buddy, or mate, and you have the damn nerve, the fucking nerve to come onto the set just when I'm about to begin a shoot. Of course, I mind! I've been working my butt off day and night. We've all been working our butts off. No one has the God damn energy to fuck around in town. Listen, pal, or mate, or what have you, you got any complaints to make, make them to the Prison's Department, make them to the mayor — don't make them to me. Now haul ass, I've got a movie to do. Jesus, I've had nothing but fucking problems since I came to this God damn town.

The boys in blue are taken aback by Al's outburst. They aren't used to bein treated like that. They look at one another, shuffle their great feet an look for a way out.

'Well, it was nothing much,' one of them says. 'We're only doing our job. Just keep your boys under control, that's all we're asking.'

'My boys, my fucking boys,' Al screams. 'What is this, the fucking deep south? They're mature men and women, not fucking kids!'

The two cops beat an asty retreat towards the gate, but as they pass Ernie, they stop beside im an one of em threatens: 'Just watch it you, you won't have that fucking Yank around for ever.'

Then Kevin puts in is two cents worth. 'Yuh know, there was this mob drinkin in Sydney, an they run outa grog. Want to get some more, but no money. So they pick on one, bit silly in the ead that one, an they tell im "Ey you, why dontcha go out and get some money for us?" The silly one scratches is ead, then says "Where?" An they tell im, "Where else dummy, but the bank." So ee gets up, staggerin a bit from the grog an goes out to a bank. It's midnight, the bank's closed, all the money's in the safe, but ee breaks a window an climbs in. Yuh know, right in front of anyone who could be lookin, an with the bloody alarms kickin up a stink. Ee gets inside an ee starts lookin for the money, but it's all locked up, then the cops come an nick him. Ee gets two years, that fella, silly in the ead alright.'

'Yeah,' I agree with im. 'An I know these other two, yuh know their names were fuckin Laurel an Ardy. They couldn't help it that was their names, ad em from their parents. Well, one night Ardy was waitin outside a pub for his friend Laurel an this police car cruises past. It goes on an around the block an comes back for a second look. Posh part of town, not many Kooris come there, an those that do don't stand around in the street. Well, the car stops an they call Ardy over to the side.

'"What are you doin here?"

'"Waitin for me mate."

'"That all you doin?"

'"Yeah."

'"Well, don't ang about all night."

'An they go off, but every now an again, they come back for a look-see. After bout an our, Laurel comes just as the cops' patience is at an end. They call both of em over.

'"What's yer name?"

'"Ardy."

'"And yours?"

'"Laurel."

'"Smart arses, eh!"

'An they get put into the back of the car an driven off to a vacant lot where they taught not to mess with the cops, but it's their names an they can't do a thing about it. An it keeps appenin all the time. They covered with scars from the beatins they get, true!'

'Oh God damn it,' Al exclaims. 'Let's all get into story-telling. Why don't you ask me for a story? Well, here's one. A special one. About this big deal I cooked up. Had this idea, big idea. Only get big ideas. Little ideas are for shmucks. And so I went and sold this idea to my bank. *Crocodile Dundee* had just made a packet in the States, and they knew that I could swing this business their way with interest and profits all round. Well, that was a year ago, and still no movie, still no profits, and that interest mounting up to high heaven. What'll I do? How can I stay in the business? I imagine that bank president on the phone nice and politely saying: "You're not reneging on our deal, Al?"

'And what am I to say to that, to him? Ask him if he's Jewish? He is, but business is business. Well, maybe. I'll just tell him. "Perhaps your bank is interested in the film business?"

'And what will he say: "We are not in the least interested in making anything but money."

'Then what do I say to him: "Too bad, cause I haven't got your money, and you, sir, are the proud owners of a half-finished film."

'So what'll happen to me. Do you think it'll swing like that? No, like hell it won't. So let's get working.'

Ee lines the cameras up for the shot. Ernie is dead serious. Ee stands outside those big double doors, an I know that ee is very aware that there is a prison be'ind me, as well as a camera. A second one down the road does a long shot of im standin there. Ee begins to walk towards that camera. If I was im I would be runnin. Al directs the first camera to begin shootin directly from the back. The shot extends into a long shot of Ernie walkin along the long low sandstone wall. Ee is a small lonely figure movin into the wide world. No jauntiness in im, an ee seems slumped in on is self. That's more like it! The festerin feelin of leavin one prison an enterin another, just like in the song. 'Prison ain't nuthin special for any Noongar, I know, for the white man makes it prison bout every place we go.'

AL: Cut, cut, that's great. Right, that's a take, now let's get the equipment onto the truck. We have to get to the university. The camera crew and I'll go ahead and shoot some exteriors. Great, Ernie, great. You're really getting into character.'

II
GOIN OME

SIX

The university as all the fakeness of istory seekin to perpetuate itself. It's built, as one of our mob says, in acclimatised mid-twenties British empire architecture. Dunno bout that, but it as a clock tower reflectin itself in a murky pool flaccid with carp. It too looks like a movie set. Al is in raptures bout it. It reminds im of the University in Phoenix, Arizona — or some out of the way cowboy place. Oh well, ee as all the exteriors ee needs to use, an The Coffee Shoppe with its white enamelled iron tables an chairs conquers im. Ee sees it as typically British. I suppose ee should know, for I don't. Anyway, the place as plenty room for the cameras an lights.

It's the university vacation an we ave the place almost to ourselves. Al as ired students of the drama society as extras. They sit around excited to be in a movie. The atmosphere is very fiftyish. The girls wear sensible twin-sets an sport permed air; the boys are in coats an trousers. There is nuthin ere of the fifties I remember: pedal pushers, tight sweaters, pegged trousers, long sports coats, long greased air an sneers, but then this is a different social scene. One I never mixed in, though I do ave it in me book an script. I find meself a seat out of the range of the cameras an sit and watch the scenes rollin past. Ardly notice the bits an pieces bein shot, as I fall into me thoughts unifyin the pieces of dialogue an actions.

Lights, camera, action. Ernie dressed in dark jeans an shirt appears at the door of the coffee shop. Obviously uneasy. Is eyes flicker about. Something pathetic about im. Ee stands there a long minute.

Al gets im to make the entrance a number of times, an ee begins to scowl. It is what Al wants. Ee shoots it. The cameras are then realigned on the girl from the beach.

June sits at a table with three young men. She glances up, sees Ernie, gets to er feet an goes to im.

June: *I've just got here. Didn't know if you would turn up, or not. I'm at that table with a few friends.*

She takes Ernie by is arm. Ee allows imself to be led to the table. Ee is introduced to the men.

June: *This is the boy I met on the beach yesterday.*

Ernie doesn't say a word. Ee sits nervously on a chair. Ee lights up a cigarette.

June: *Frank and Bill here are doing Social Anthropology. They are really interested in the plight of the Aborigines . . .*

Even though I ave written these lines, I inwardly shudder at em. I know what's comin, ave bin in such scenes, an know the whole thing. This'll be their first meetin with an Aborigine, an ee'll be expected to be cluey on all aspects of what I've written as 'the plight of the Aborigines'. Naturally, I've written it to show what we come up against from even well-meanin whites. Ernie squirms in is chair. There's a few takes an cuts, an this disrupts the questionin. Still it goes on.

Ernie: *Why?*

Bill (or is it Frank): *I'm planning to do a project on the Austral Grove experiment. Do you know of it?*

Ernie nods.

Bill: *Well, that's fine. Naturally, I plan to contact the local Aboriginal leaders on how it is working out, but I would like your opinion on whether it will help to integrate the Aborigines into the wider Australian community?*

I wonder if Al will later on discard the whole scene. It sounds phoney. Only problem is they do talk like that, an do ask such questions, an do wait with bated breath to get the info directly from the orse's mouth. We all know ow it is an ow to play this game. Most of us go along with it, though maybe some'll ave better answers than the ones I've written.

It reminds me of a story that shows just ow well we are integrated into the general community. Yuh know, when the oldies get a little charged, they sometimes start arguin an end up callin a bloke out. This appened to this ol bloke. Ee was really gettin stuck into this other bloke, mind you only with words, not with fists, an the other guy couldn't take it any longer, so ee says: 'Right, I've ad enough, yuh come along to the park tomorra an we'll settle it.' The bloke who ad bin doin the stirrin agreed: 'Yer on, I'll be there, first thing tomorra mornin.' Well, mornin comes an the bloke is still wild, still wantin to do im, but when ee finally does turn up, is arm's all plastered an in a sling. 'Sorry, mate, can't fight yuh with me arm like this. Last night, this bloody car it me an done this to me arm.' Well, no fight, but yuh know what that ol codger done? Ee didn't wanta be in no fight, an so ee went to the ospital, ad a lation workin there, an ee gets er to plaster up is arm, that's what ee done, an that's what I call bein integrated into the system.

Now it's Ernie's turn to come up against these

questions. Ee begins an I notice that ee's changed is accent so that ee is close to mimickin the students. That's what I mean about livin in two worlds an learnin ow to camouflage yer speech an manners when it suits yuh.

> **Ernie:** *The answer of course lies in the question. Some of the people in the Grove are really tryin to make it a success, others are pullin them down as usual, then there's the drink . . .*

Ernie appears cool an detached, but in such a situation we're all ears an eyes, readin the situation an waitin for it to become an all white scene — an it usually does!

> **Frank:** *And what would the question be in such a situation and how would we implement the answer? There must be a way!*
> **Bill:** *We must give them decent conditions as a pre-requisite —*
> **Frank:** *But what are decent conditions — for them?*
> **Bill:** *Naturally, the first thing would be the granting of citizenship rights —*
> **Frank:** *Yes, definitely, though programmes must be formulated to ease the transition. Can a person who's been living under a tree or in a humpy know how to manage a decent home?*
> **Bill:** *They must be educated —*
> **Frank:** *And let's not forget that the wider community must be educated to accept them.*

This is just one side of the white syndrome, but I've also written a scene for another kind of white. It's what yuh could call the nigger lover. The lush-bodied girl Renee is to play that part. I'm interested in seein ow she andles it. It's a bit close to the bone. She readies for er entrance, if yuh call it that, an she glances towards me. I see she's nervous an smile. She doesn't notice, too busy tensin erself up. She's dressed as a beatnik, er air flowin bout er face whitened with make-up. Er clothes is black: black skirt, black floppy sweater an black stockins. She does look the part, though she might've worn sunglasses, but that doesn't matter. Now she walks to the table an stands there, white an intense with passionate concern for the Aboriginal.

Girl: *Yes, it's white people who need the education, not the native.*

She glances across at Ernie who gives no sign that ee as eard.

Frank: *That is what I am saying.*
Girl: *Please . . . I consider it stupid and arrogant to want to drag the Aborigines into our so-called civilisation. Why, why it is like giving a jazz musician a classical music education. It'll only spoil their natural ability. We ourselves must regain that naturalness before it is too late. We should be learning from the Aborigines, not the other way round.*
Bill: *But the problems? . . .*
June: *Today I handed in my paper at last. I was given an extension, but even then I had to stay up all last night to get it done on time.*
Girl: *You know what a friend told me today. He said that there is a regulation that if you do not agree with the mark given, you can apply to have your paper re-examined by another lecturer. It's a fact.*

Ernie switches off. Ee as bin well an truly left out. Ee stares towards a paintin on the far wall. It is titled: *Man In Revolt of Exile* an is a mass of colour splashed over geometric shapes. Suddenly, ee smiles, though not the carefree smile ee would've given em a day ago, then is face assumes an intense expression roughly modelled on the one the girl ad when she entered the conversation.

Ernie: *That painting there. It reminds me of a book I have recently finished reading. There is the same mood of, well, of bitter despair and dark melancholy.*

I watch as Ernie's eyes move from student to student. Ee as gotten into me script. A camera sights on the paintin. A close-up. Al murmurs, 'beautiful; beautiful'. Ee whispers 'cut' to the first camera an signals to camera two to focus in on a long-aired type who as taken no part in the precedin conversation.

Ernie (off-screen): *Or am I being too psychological?*

The bait is taken.

Dorian (The long-haired type): *No, no, no! You're right. Action painting is all psychic upheaval: rage, anger, despair, frustration — throwing yourself into the sea of the mind and pulling out the fishes of emotion. Do you paint by any chance?*
Ernie: *Tried my hand at landscapes —*
Girl: *Oh, landscapes!* (She yawns.) *Haven't seen you in here before — are you a student?*
June: *I asked him along to see the Uni. He's thinking of joining us next year.*
Dorian: *I say, I'm having a soiree at my studio tonight. Come along, you're welcome.*
June: *He'd like that. It'll give him a chance to meet people.*

She smiles at Ernie, who shrugs.

June: *Dorian's evenings are loads of fun . . .*

Al whispers. 'Cut' an congratulates everyone. The

shootin is over, that is until the evenin, but that will be back at the prison. We all ave coffee an I find the lush-bodied girl Renee beside me. I tell er that I liked er actin. I'm tryin to be nice, but then she was pretty good. But she's modest an tells me that Kylie is the one who as everythin going for er, an that this is er first role.

'Yeah, includin an Aboriginal name,' I reply.

'Why, is Kylie Aboriginal? She was named after a famous woman writer, Kylie Tennant.'

'Yeah, met er a long time ago. Never did get to read any of er books. But Kylie is our word for boomerang — anyway yer got a lot goin for yuh too, Ernie for instance?'

'Ernie? What do you mean?'

'Oh, nuthin much.'

'Anyway, he's gone a little strange since last night. He's not his self and seems to be avoiding me. Not your doing, is it?'

'Nuthin to do with me. . . . Anyway gettin back to yer actin, yuh make a real fine Uni student, must've bin one?'

'I was. What sort of education did you have? I find it difficult to read you. Your books are not what I would expect from you.'

'Do yuh really wanta know? Well, I was at Swanview, it's a boys' ome not far from ere. Might even take yuh to see it. There's these Spanish-style buildins, all cream-walled an red-tiled. It's beside a river an right on the bank is the playin field. I ad to play games there. Ad to do everythin in teams too. Yuh know, march in teams, play sports in teams, eat in teams, shit in teams, shower in teams, sleep in teams. Yuh name it, we done it in teams. I ate teams. It was a Catholic dump run by the Irish brothers an it was an awful place. We even made up a song to celebrate it.

> Mummy, daddy take me way,
> From this awful place one day,
> No more eatin stew like glue,
> No more eatin bread like poo.

'I was sent to that place when I was only nine. They took me away from me mum, an sent me there. That's the story of me life, sent ere, sent there, sent everywhere. They never ever let me decide anythin for meself. It was all done for me, almost everythin that is. I did try to nick off from that place. Got up late one night. Everythin was pitch dark, yuh know, scary! But I ated that place; wanted to get back ome to me mum. Well, I got to the road, was walkin along it feelin free, then this car comes along. I duck off the road quick smart, but not quick enough I suppose, for the car screeches to an alt, an it's full of those brothers. They toss me into it an I'm back in the ome — some home! Got punished for that, six of the best on me backside. Never cried though, just let the atred well up inside of me instead of tears. But somethin else appened inside too. I never tried it again. So I stayed an got used to it; so I stayed until they ad to chuck me out into the wide world. I was scared of that by then, an I ended up in Greystones, good old Freo, just like a lot of us kids did. Yuh know, we talk about goin down the river. Yuh start up the Cannin at Castlemain when yuh real young, then at nine or so, yuh get floated down to Swanview, then when yer sixteen they fling yuh in the river an yuh drift right down to Freo. That's ow it was for me.'

'Gee, you must've had it tough?'

'Not that tough. Anyway, forget it! Yuh make a swell beatnik. Ad a beatnik girlfriend once, Lillian, all red air, but she fucked everyone. That was in the days when free love was the thing to believe in. Some done it too. By the way, what's yer name? We was introduced, but names enter one ear an go out the other.'

'Renee Appleby.'

'Thought so. Just wanted to ear it from yuh.'

'God, you're impossible!'

'I'm not that bad.'

'You're something else, truly!'

'So are you, I'm waitin for the shootin tonight. Yuh know yer in the love scene. I'll be watchin to see how yuh make out. It'll be like a re'earsal for the real thing.'

'God!'

'Come on, don't get all eated up.'

'You're the living end!'

'Come on, yuh can't take on a black in an argument. Yuh can't argue like we do. Yuh know ow we do it? We say: "Well, fuck yuh" — then stalk off. That's our answer to everythin: "Fuck yuh!". Now all that remains is for me to stalk off.'

'But you know, your words hurt me!'

'Maybe, they do, but who pushed who into the water?' . . .

She laughs, an I grin back a wide-eyed grin I've captured from some past. She is a real beautiful girl, an just as she said about Kylie, all that yuh should love.

SEVEN

Back in jail for our last an final scene. Still gives me the willies, bein ere an all that. Guess it'll always affect me like that, makin me relive all that shit, all that turmoil. Still I wrote a book bout it, made a script bout it — so fuckin what? Get it outa me system once an for all. Just somethin to see on the big screen, unreal, baby, unreal! An they all set up to do the party. Some party, but the chapel is ideal. Those rafters an things, those white-washed walls now ung with those god awful paintins. Still there's that smell bout the place. Smell of prison; smell of prison soap; smell of fear; smell of commands issued an obeyed. Smell of kids bein fucked into stupid lives by so-called men. Yuh know what appened to me mate, a Swan boy too! Well, ee was on the pretty side. Soft. Unable to stick up for isself. Ready to take a fall an keep on fallin down where the birdies don't fly. Yuh know, Christmas was special in jail. Yeah, we eard stories months before the main event, about it, an what we could expect. Yeah, an it wasn't about the plum duff they served for Christmas dinner either. Yuh see, as a special concession, they for this one day of the year left all the doors, the doors between the divisions an the cell doors unlocked. Yuh might think that was a taste of freedom, but for us kids it was look out for your arse time. The men cons came untin out the weak ones an the young'uns. An if they managed to get yuh in a cell all by yerself, or managed to drag yuh inside, yuh became the woman for em. Big deal for em, but after that yuh were marked for a different time of sentence: bum boy for those arse bandits who could drag yuh out of a screw's sight.

Great, huh? Us kids were sentenced twice, an no wonder we were scared. Well, that first Christmas I spent inside, we ad our day of freedom, an me mate was caught by a mob who came from the Main Division. They got im in a cell an the lot went through im. It was the end for im. After the shaggin ee went queer an that meant ee was lost to us. We ad to work with im an say good day to im, but we couldn't afford to be friendly with im. Yuh know the expression 'splattered with the same shit'? Well, somethin smelly like that, an to be seen to be friends with a queer was to be labelled as one too — or to be is lover. Anyway ee was shagged an became a strange sorta eddy in our midst. Somethin that shamed us. We were glad when ee was caught with a guy an put into segregation. Segregation was where they put the queers an the vicious ones. They ad their own little cell, an their own little exercise yard. They lived all alone an were in jail within a jail. This appened to me mate.

Remember one time, I was comin back from the Admin block an ad to pass through the Main Division. The segregation cells were on the ground floor an, as I passed em, I stopped an decided to look through the eye-ole to see ow ee was makin out. I looked through that ole an saw im there, but changed. Ee ad taken some of the red off a book cover, soaked the dye out, an used it on is lips. They looked strange as if they were all bloody. I shuddered an urried away without sayin a word. Ee was lost to us. An so, what were queers to me, but weakies who allowed emselves to be caught an fucked. They ad lost the right to be considered male, ad lost the right to mateship, an were there to be abused by guys like Ralph who were not right in the ead. This is what I learnt bout queers in jail. Poofters were dead ends of the road, an no one wanted to end up like that. No one! So they were somethin yuh didn't like an didn't wanta mix with. Yer educated in jail an what yuh learn yuh keep in yer ead an eart for ever after. That's ow prison affects yuh about things. Still, later I did mix with some, an me character, Dorian, is based on one of em, an artist bloke I spoke to through a glass wall.

'Well, well, the great writer moping as usual?'

I stare at Renee an manage a smile. 'Just thinkin bout this scene, that's all I ave to do round here, just think. Don't know why I'm ere? Maybe to add to the atmosphere. Anyway, I'm glad to see yuh. I like beatnik girls. As I told yuh, me first real girlfriend was some sorta beatnik. She paraded round with me cause I was an Abo —'

'You mean she wan't taken in by your charm?'

'No, that wasn't what interested er! Anyway stay cool. That was the operational word in those days. Cool it, man, an all that jazz. I liked those few beatniks I met though. Yuh know, artists an people like that. Might've bin em that put the idea in me ead to write.'

'You mean that you owe them something? You don't show it in the film, dig!'

'What do yuh mean?'

'They're not very human, or understanding —'

'They weren't! Anyway if yuh feel that yer uman an understandin, feel like that in yer actin.'

'I'm trying to do that. It's just a little scene, not any great piece to get your teeth into. Still, dig, it'll come across okay. Yuk, there goes my stomach again. It's always like this before. Your stomach literally begins to squirm.

'Know the feelin, chick, know the feelin.'

'Hey, I got this riddle. If beatnik women were called "chicks" what were beatnik men called?'

'Cats cuz they ate the chicks.'

'Is that the answer, I forget, you know it's this damn stomach —'

'Yuh forget. Well, sorta. . . . Ow's this for a beatnik poem: "I saw the best minds of my generation destroyed by madness, starving hysterical naked, dragging themselves through the negro streets at dawn looking for an angry fix."'

'What was that?'

'Poetry.'

'Yours?'

'No, Ginsberg, a beatnik an one of the best an worse, dig?'

'Dig, oh where's Ernie? I want to get it over with!'

'I'm lookin forward to seein yuh two together?'

'So am I. I want to get it over and done with.'

'Yuh know, just to see ow you make love.'

'You call that love under lights. Man, I like it with the lights down low. Why isn't Al getting ready?!'

'Ee was with Jinda last time I saw im.'

'He was, was he!'

'Yep, she's is cousin.'

'Some cousin! There he is now. Lights, action, and over.'

This is a drinkin scene an Al likes to use real booze. Says that it gets the best outa us. I go an elp meself to a glass of red wine. Stand an sip it while watchin Al gettin is crew, or as one of is atrocious puns would ave it 'is screw, cause anything that they can screw up, they screw up', together. I see that Renee as found Ernie an that Jinda as put space between em. I take over a glass of wine to er.

'Yuh must be bored, not avin anythin to do until tomorrow.'

'It doesn't matter. I get to see how a film is made. It's good experience.'

'Yeah, suppose it is. Yuh know seein me book takin life is really somethin. Now when I think of me characters, they look like the people who are playin em. They no longer belong to me.'

'So you'll see me as Denise, from now on?'

'Yeah, long as yuh play er right.'

'I'll try to.'

'Just play it low key an it'll be fine.'

'I'll remember that.'

'Quiet on the set. Ready, cameras rolling, take one.'

I watch on the same inevitability of take after take to final take, each goin towards makin up a composite scene. If I didn't know the script, I wouldn't be able to follow me story, but cause I do, I can put it together. Ernie stands framed in the doorway lookin forlorn an outa place. Ee's nervous an waitin for the action to commence so that ee can put on a mask. Dorian comes in from one side of the camera an slaps im on the shoulder. Ernie whirls, then relaxes warily. *Cut!*

Cameras cut between Dorian an Ernie's faces durin the ensuin dialogue. There is time out for muffed lines an Al is beginnin to get steamed up. Well, it should all fit together. That's is job, ain't it!

Dorian: *Glad that you could make it. Come in and get yourself a drink. Later on, I want to show you the latest oil I'm working on.*

Ernie: *I can see where the grog is. Mainly came to see someone. . . .*

Dorian: *Well, you're easy to satisfy, aren't you? I'll see you later.*

CUT.

June (off-screen): *Good boy—you made it.*

The camera which as bin on Ernie adjusts to include June in the shot. Ee stares at er noticin that she's still wearin the same clothes as in the previous scene. She catches the direction of is eyes.

June: *No rest for the wicked—uh, I mean no time to go home and change. I live a dog's life sometimes.*

Ernie: *Some dog and some life.*
June: *Okay, okay, the chip on the shoulder becomes you; but this is the first party I've been to in months. I'm out to enjoy myself.*
Ernie: *Same for me too. Eighteen months ard labour.*
June: *Hard labour for me too.*
Ernie: *Wouldn't know bout that.*
June: *Wouldn't you?*
Ernie: *No!*
June: *Well, I would.*
Ernie: *You don't know nuthin!*
June: *Just like you—can't you see that it is possible to change?*
Ernie: *No!*

Jazz music begins an couples begin dancin.

Ernie: *Yuh wanta dance?*
June: *You do know how to?*
Ernie: *Social grace I learnt in the orphanage I went to. Might tell yuh bout that sometime. It's funny—in a sad way.*

They move to the music in a quick twostep. They pass Dorian doin an exaggerated dance of is own devisin. Ee flashes a bright smile at Ernie who looks away.

June: *I see you don't like Dorian?*
Ernie: *Ee's okay. Bit of a queer though.*
June: *And you're not, not queer, eh?*
Ernie: *No!*

Ernie breaks out of the dance an goes to the table where the drinks are. Ee pours himself a wine.

June stands in the middle of the floor. She looks after im, then shrugs. A man approaches her. She smiles an dances with im.

Ernie follows the example of other people an sits on

the floor with is back against the wall. Ee sits near the drinks table. Ee puts is glass on the floor beside im, pulls out a cigarette an lights up. Thelonious Monk's 'Misterioso' begins to play. Is and begins movin to the rhythm.

Renee dressed as ee is in black comes to get a glass of wine. Er face is made-up into a dead white mask, though the eyes ave bin marked out in black as as er mouth. She examines Ernie, then sits beside im.

Ernie glances at er, then away. Is face is expressionless.

The girl's face is expressionless. She glances at im.

Renee: *You dig Monk, don't you? I dig him too.*
Ernie: *Dig him like I was diggin my grave.*
Renee: *Hey, that's gas, man.*
Ernie: *Each note is a spadeful of dirt on my coffin.*
Renee: *They cover us.*
Ernie: *My scream is the silence of my life.*
Renee: *Never to have been heard.*
Ernie: *To have lived is not enough for me.*
Renee: *I want to be heard, I want to be heard!*
Ernie: *To be dead is not enough for me.*
Renee: *Nor me, man, nor me!*

She sags against Ernie an giggles. She's drunk. Ernie sips is drink, an looks up at two legs, then a bendin face. It is Dorian.

Dorian: *Well, before we get nicely settled, I'd like to show you the painting.*
Ernie: *Just point it out, man, I can see them from here, muddy boots and all.*
Dorian: *It's unfinished. I've put it away from, from little grubby hands and minds.*
Renee: *Yeah, little grubby minds all right, dear!*
Dorian: *I was hoping that you could suggest a title?* —
Ernie: *Why not call it* Queer World, *that should fit it.*

Renee giggles wildly. Dorian looks at her angrily an walks off in an uff.

Renee: *That fixed old Dorian, won't be invited to his next party, but who cares. He's so square.*
Ernie: *Dunno about that, ad a mate who ended up like im. Ee was in boob with me.*
Renee: *Boob? What's that?*
Ernie: *Arrh, just a new style of blues, just a new style of blues.*
Renee: *Never heard of it.*
Ernie: *Maybe I'll tell you about it — later . . .*
Renee (singing):
> *Trouble in mind, I'm blue,*
> *But I won't be blue always,*
> *Cause the sun gonna shine*
> *In my back door some day. . . .*

God, I'm plastered, you know DRUNK!

She punches Ernie lightly on the arm.

Renee: *Got to, got to go — give me a hand up, won't you?*

Ernie gets to is feet. Ee steadies imself, reaches down an pulls er up. They stand swayin.

Renee: *Got an idea, gas of an idea, let's go and see old Dorian's painting. I know where it is.*
Ernie: *Lead the way, doll, lead the way.*

June stands talkin to a man near the entrance. She watches Ernie an Renee movin towards her.

June: *Just a moment, I must see that boy before he goes.*
Man: *Didn't know you went for the beatnik type?*
June: *He's no beatnik. I have to see him. Excuse me.*

She meets Ernie an Renee.

June (to Ernie): *Not off already, are you?*
Ernie: *When yuh gotta go, yuh gotta go.*
June: *We didn't finish our conversation. I thought we might pick it up now.*
Ernie: *Already picked up somethin better.*
June: *Or worse?*
Ernie: *What're yuh gettin at?*
Renee: *Forget about her. I'm bursting.*
Ernie: *Go a'ead, I'll catch up.*
Renee: *Hey, I can't do it on my own.*
June: *I can see that brains isn't one of your strong points.*
Renee: *I know you.*
Ernie: *What'd yuh mean? I did me matric in boob, that's brains for yuh.*
June: *That's what I wanted to talk to you about.*
Renee: *Hey, lay off, we gotta go.*
June: *You can go!*
Renee: *I know you and your talks.*
June: *Oh, get lost!*
Ernie: *No, we're both goin, we can talk some other time.*

He shoves June out of the way.

Ernie: *Get back to yer friends an ave a good time.*

The man has been watchin em from near the entrance. Ee rushes forward.

Man: *Anything wrong, June?*
Ernie: *Who are you?*
June: *No, we're just saying goodnight.*
Ernie: *Who are you?*
Man: *I might ask the same question.*
Ernie: *Get fucked!*

Suddenly ee its the man full in the face with is fist. The man falls, then jumps up. Renee screams, an runs outa the room.

Man: *Why you —*
Ernie: *Come on, come on!*
June: *Stop it — both of you!* (to Ernie) *Please apologise to him.*
Ernie: *Never pologised in me life, for nuthin!*

Ee walks out.

Man: *Where did you meet him!*

CUT.

The end of the shootin an where is the fuckin love scene? I was waitin patiently for it an it never appened. Al must've cut it out. No wonder ee says 'cut' so often. No bloody wonder! I make me way towards where ee's talkin to the cameramen. Ee's real appy an smilin. Kevin comes to im before I can get to im an begins one of is stories. I stop an laugh to meself. It doesn't matter. Just a movie. Only wanted to see ow Renee made out. No skin off me nose, if I don't. Maybe I'll get to act in the real thing later on, maybe not knowin er. . . .

Decide to go an talk to Ernie, tell im what a good job ee's doin, an ow ee's got the dialogue down pat. Yuh know, yuh ave to be like a chameleon in yer speech. Mimic their style of talkin, but when yer ad too much yuh find yerself usin yer own language. Yuh stop pretendin an be yer natural self when yuh want out, an there's nuthin to be gained suckin up to em. That's ow I writ the dialogue, an that's ow Ernie is speakin it. Must come natural to im, just as it comes natural to all of us.

Ain't going to get to Ernie tonight, for as I get to where ee's standin with Renee, I ear er say, 'Well, fuck you!' Ernie stamps off in the direction of Jinda. I reply for im: 'Yuh learnin.'

She doesn't answer, er eyes are on Ernie an Jinda. Er ead turns to watch em go out.

'They cousins,' I tell her. 'Kissin cousins.'

'Are they,' she answers.

'Yeah, they're renewin their acquaintances. Liked ow yuh played yer role tonight. Just like the real thing. Ow'd yuh like actin as if yuh were about to piss yer pants? Sorry, bout the love scene. Seems like Al's cut it, or ee's doin it another time. No one tells me a thing. If I ad me way, yuh'd be fuckin in all the scenes.'

'Oh Christ, can't you shut up!'

'Somethin on yer mind? Don't worry, Ernie's true blue.'

'Why don't you fuck off!'

'Yuh really are learnin the lingo. I'll piss off. I'll go and ask Al if the big scene between Ernie an Jinda is still in. Never can tell with these Yanks an their fuckin "this won't sell, and that will" kind of mentality. See yuh.'

I go towards Al an Kevin. Ee tells me that the milk-bar scenes an the love scene between Ernie an Jinda are scheduled for tomorrow.

Kevin pricks up his ears at the mention of the love scene, an is pixie face wrinkles as ee begins another story. Sometimes I wonder where ee gets em from, or ow ee keeps em in mind for, with me, they enter one ear an go out t'other, but some can tell a story an others can't. I'm one of the ones that can't.

'Yuh see there was this woman, up north Queensland, Mt Isa way, an one night she's goin ome an these white blokes jump er, rape er, yuh know. Well, it gets to the legal service an they get the blokes charged. Well, the lawyer bloke gets, let's call er Mary, to tell im what appened to er. "Well," she sez. "I was walkin ome an these three white fellas gin to follow me. They come after me an grab me. They fling me on the ground an one of these fellas, ee pulls out his cock, puts it in me cunt an begins fuckin me. I lay there, can't do nuthin bout it. Three fellas too many for me to andle."

'The lawyer listens, then shakes is ead. "Mary, yuh
know yuh tellim me that story, bout what appened. Now
if yuh come before the judge an yuh tellim like that, well
the judge won't like it. Yuh tellim different way. Now
instead of 'cock' yuh say 'penis' an instead of 'cunt' yuh
say 'vagina' an instead of 'fucking' yuh say 'intercourse'.
Yuh tellim like that in court, yuh savvy?" Mary goes over
the details with im an tells im, "I say it like yuh tellin
me to." So the day of the trial arrives an Mary gets into
the witness box to give er evidence. She begins to tell er
story. "I was walkin ome when these three white fellas
gin followin me. I run, but they catch me up an fling me
on the ground. I lyin on ground an one of them takes out
his penis an begins to ave, ave intercourse with me. You
know ee puts his penis in me, in me"—an she looks
across at the lawyer an calls out, "Ey, what was that word
yuh toldim me to call me cunt?"'

Al an I burst out laughin, an Al begins to reply with
one of is own stories. Ee's mellowin out. I begin to listen,
then look across an see that Renee is still standin where I
left er. I go across to er an say: 'Sorry for speakin outa
turn. Shouldn't ave done it. Just an abit of mine. Forgive
an forget, eh?'

'Maybe,' she says, then smiles an lashes out. 'One thing
you should know is that you can't write for nuts. Al had
to rewrite most of your script, didn't he?'

'What do yuh think white people are for, to look after
us poor black people. We ave the ideas, they ave the unger
for the money. Yuh know the only guy who ever made
any money outa writin about Aborigines was a white
bloke.'

'I'm sorry, I shouldn't have said that.'

'Why not? Anyway, yuh goin to ang around ere all
night? Still early an yuh got nuthin to lose, so let's go for
a stroll?'

We go outa those big prison gates, an suddenly I flash a
smile at Renee. A weight drops off me shoulders. Me
back begins to straighten, an I mutter to meself, 'I'm

gettin too old to carry a chip the size of a log for the rest
of me days.'

'What?'

'Nuthin to do with yuh, only about ow suddenly yuh
start to grow up, what's the word, mature, an yuh start to
sort through yer past, an fling away what yuh don't need
any more.'

'Is that what you're doing?'

'I think so. Yuh can't carry the weight of the world on
yer shoulders for ever, an then some of the things I done,
I done cause of me, not cause of the world.'

'Oh, I suppose you do eventually have to take re-
sponsibility for your own life and actions.'

'Yuh know, yuh sound just like June in the movie.'

'Do I?'

'Yeah, accent an all. Yer a know-all, yuh know that?!'

'No.'

'Yer all are, that's what I ate about yuh. It seems that
yuh come into this world knowin what to do. Well, the
rest of us as to learn, an while we learnin we ave to get by
the best we can. It's like that, yuh know?'

'No, I don't know! You just assume a lot.'

'Maybe I do, maybe . . . Let's change the subject. The
river's just down a ways from ere. Nice night tonight cept
for the mossies. Just down these steps an along ere. I like
rivers flowin in the night.'

As I've said before, Fremantle is all done up these days,
an this goes for the river bank. As I walk across the lawn
to the water's edge, I can't elp thinkin about me lifelong
trip down the river, an ow I'm still stuck at the mouth of
it after twenty years or so. Then Renee, just like a woman,
plants one of er igh eels into the soft earth beneath the
grass an stumbles just like Denise ad long ago. She grabs
at me an er lush body, er garden body is sinkin into mine.
We come together for a long moment. It's Denise over
again, an I know that we'll make love some time or other.
That sex thing is oldin us together. Then she pulls away
an walks an sits on the stone wall tamin the river. I

stand a little be'ind er feeling as lonely as the lights streakin cross the dark water, each separate an distinct, but it is a good feelin for all that. We sit side by side quietly, not sayin a word. Fremantle as a wonderful climate an nights warm with achin. Achin with the pain I felt standin at the window of me cell starin out at the dark sea an earin from be'ind bars the ebb an flow of the freedom sea. I ear the lap of the waters an begin tellin er bout the time I was gettin out of prison an instead of feelin appy just felt sad.

'Yuh know, I ad no one to go to. Well, they marched us into the Admin block after we ad showers an ad put on our goin out into the wide world suits. They were awful, but the super was wearin one that looked like it ad bin made up in the prison tailorin shop too. That made me wild. I didn't want to look even a bit like im. Ee was, well yer still dressed in yer beatnik gear, ee was what we called square, an nuthin we wanted to be. Ee also looked as if ee was doin a life sentence too an so didn't inspire any sort of respect. None of the screws did. Well, ee anded us each a little brown envelope containin our lousy pay: just enough to buy a few drinks. An as ee anded out the envelopes is mouth twisted into a little smile. It was as if ee was sayin: "See yuh soon, mate, see yuh soon." An yuh know, ee did see me soon. Too soon, an I was there when ee retired. God, that fuckin prison, those fuckin bars, those fuckin screws, those fuckin cons. God, I couldn't do it again. I'd rather die, end it all, than go back into one of those places!'

'Was it hard,' Renee whispers, an er and enters mine. It comforts me. I need somethin to cling to, to cling to as the bitterness of those years drains away into that dark river water bitter with the blood an piss an tears of old cons like me.

'Yuh know, there are blokes who can't stand the outside. Can't take it at all. They come in for five years say, then one day they are eaved out. They out one day, then in the next. An ol mate of mine was like that. The screws even useta keep is cell for im. But I wasn't like that. I was one of em that, as soon as got out, found a room an oled up in it. Used to stay in it all day an every day. Dashin out, gettin a flagon or two of cheap wine, then rushin back to me refuge. Yuh know, I couldn't andle anythin. Cars an buses, shops an streets. I remember goin into a supermarket. Seein all those goods on the shelves, same kinda things with different brand names put me into a fright. Man, I was shiverin. Couldn't make a choice, didn't know ow to. All those things just pressin in on me. I couldn't take it, just couldn't ack it.'

'But you wrote those books?'

'Yeah, inside. Kept me from goin crazy, kept me from seein the long years stretchin a'ead. Now one of em's bein made into this movie, an I'm in boob again!'

I stare at the waters. All the city sounds are distant just as they filter through into me cell. Different world out ere, an I shiver an feel that old panic I thought I ad gotten over. It's only Renee's and that keeps me from leapin up an runnin, just runnin. I turn into er eyes an we exchange a kiss. Tonight, I couldn't fuck if me life depended on it, but it doesn't an Renee is only givin me comfort, just as others ave given me comfort, just as Denise as given me comfort.

I smile into er eyes, an that smile becomes the carefree grin I must've ad once. I even sing: 'The night is young and you're so beautiful.'

Then we get up an walk an ead back towards the great sleepin beast of the prison. I could never go back inside for real. This time I'm sayin *goodbye* for ever!

EIGHT

Yuh know, I'm what's called institutionised, bin in one place or another most of me life, an it appened from the age of nine when I found meself in Swanview. There I done me basic trainin on ow to exist ina institution. Yuh got two fists an add to it a thinkin brain an yuh survive. Yuh learn ow to andle it, an don't let it andle yuh. Well from Swanview me life became one institution after t'other, or rather I made it to the big one of Freo, an that might've bin the end of the road, if I adn't ad some sort of thinkin brain that told me sometimes at night, that this was no place for me, no place no way! Still before that . . .

I get outa Swanview, or rather am pushed out when I reach fifteen. Naturally by then I can't fend for meself, an so they get the Catholic Welfare to elp me. They get me a job an a place to stay in an ouse that specialises in puttin up coloured people. There's a couple more stayin along with me, but after the ome an bein outa that ome, I think there must be somethin more to the outside. I get outa that place, find meself another one across the tracks on the wild side of town, an then the job gets rid of me, an I've to use me wits to survive. It's pretty easy, but I ate bein on me own. Then one night I wander into the Royal Milk-bar, an feel a bit at ome. No one lays anythin on me, an Alphonse the Ponce who runs the place likes kids who don't cause im any trouble. Guess ee wants to be the big daddy of us all. If ee knew yuh, ee even sold yuh a drink from the wine bottles ee kept under the counter. Of course, ee wants another kind of payment too, an every now an again ee takes an andful of tit offa one of the girls; but only if ee knows er. All in all ee is a good bloke, an cagey too. All ee as for the cops is a 'good day' an a vacant smile. Nuthin else, for as I've said ee's a good bloke.

Well, that time I wandered in there, I was outa place. Like I liked the atmosphere, but the kids there was different. They all wore better clothes than I did, long sports jackets and narrow pegged pants to go with their narrow ties. They also ad longer air too. Yer know combed straight back to end in a groove at the back, an a curl danglin over the forehead, just like I described to Ernie. We were the first ones to wear jeans in this town, man! First ones, for we considered ourselves sharp dressers — cool threads an a cool manner was the order of the day. Even Alphonse the Ponce copied our style though ee was way outa our age. Ee ad a brother who ran the sharpest clothin store in town. We got our clothes there. Well, most of em. Trouble was with all this attention to our gear, we couldn't get into fights. Ow could yuh? Yuh'd mess yer clothing an untidy yer air. So we tried to keep outa fights. Most of us at least — me, only maybe, but then I was a stupid kid. Yer stupid not to play it cool! . . .

Well, I remember as if it was just yesterday, when I'm sittin with me mate Chinky in the milk-bar. Yuh know just sittin there an feelin good in me long white sports jacket, me narrow striped tie an me black shirt. Me air was just right too. It ad taken me ours in front of the mirror to get it greased back just right. Man, I felt I was perfect, then the door opens an this bloke walks in. Me face moves up, an down. Just a thick old bloke, an the jukebox is playin me favourite number: 'Jukebox Baby'. It stops just as this bloke comes in. Is steps don't sound as loud as the silence. I get up to get another number goin to cover it. I am there at that old record machine fumblin

for the coin, when a eavy and drops on me shoulder, an I
freeze. 'This is it, I tell meself, not identifyin the 'this' or
the 'it'.

The bloke's deep voice rumbles: 'Well, well just the kid
I came to see. You've gotten yourself a little trip to do
with me as your guide.'

I try to wriggle outa is grip. It tightens. I get, I feel real
scared. Is grip tightens. It urts. I wince, then stop
strugglin. Be cool, man!

I say to the bloke: 'Mind if I play a number for me
mates fore I go?'

Ee says nuthin, but ee's not shovin me at the door. So I
feed a last coin in, an get a song. I'll always remember the
words. Always, it was me favourite.

Jukebox baby, seventeen, graduated and got that twist.

Jukebox baby, seventeen, seventeen, seventeen —

Oh fuck, don't remember em words no more, but
seventeen for me was a bad age, an guess where I ended
up? Juvenile Court!

Me probation officer, Mr Robinson was there with is
shit advice. I keep noddin as ee whispers: 'Now listen
carefully. Don't give the magistrate any lip, understand!
No answering back, just speak when you're spoken to. Be
sure to call the magistrate, "Sir". Be polite and you'll
most likely get off on a bond.'

I keep noddin to is dumb advice. I'm so scared that I
believe even im.

Ee takes me to a table an we sit. The magistrate enters
an we stand. I see that ee is a pompous little bloke, a little
squirt much shorter than I am. Nervousness gets me an I
give a sorta snigger of a giggle. Robinson glares at me.
We sit an they call up the first witness. The demon lover
who took me from me mates at the milk-bar.

ATTENDANT; You swear to tell the truth, the whole
truth, and nothing but the truth?

DETECTIVE: I do, sir.

MAGISTRATE: The things, the exhibits you see on the
table, you found them in the boy's possession?

DETECTIVE: Yes, sir, with the exception of the, of the cosh. This was found at the scene of the crime.

MAGISTRATE: The court has your statement, we'll recall you if we have further questions.

DETECTIVE: Yes, sir.

MAGISTRATE: It is understood that the boy is at present on probation. Would the probation officer please present his report.

I can feel Robinson gettin to is feet. Ee said that ee'd elp me but, as ee speaks, I realise ee's done the dirty on me. Yuh can't trust the dirty bastards one bit. Well, fuck im, I don't care, care, care!

ROBINSON: Sir, unfortunately there is little that can be said for this boy. The Child Welfare Department has had nothing but trouble from him since his release from Swanview Boys' Home. At the age of nine he was sent there for breaking and entering a number of stores in the country town in which he was then living with his mother. The family to put it mildly were a bunch of drifters. It appears that he did settle in at the Boys' Home, except for an attempt to abscond. Reports show that he was not unintelligent, and he was quite good at school. At the beginning of last year, he was released and placed under the guidance of the Catholic Welfare. They found him a decent job in a garage and accommodation in a boarding house which specialises in Catholic children. Unfortunately, with the restraining environment of the Boys' Home removed, he immediately began to go bad. He left the house and didn't turn up at his job. It was when he was arrested on a car stealing charge that he came under my care. I found him a job and accommodation, but he left these almost immediately. I understand that he drifted into a native settlement and remained there for some time. He is of Aboriginal descent, on his mother's side, and I believe that this goes a long way towards explaining his behaviour. Sadly, there are more than a few cases like his. He next surfaced in the Northbridge part of the city where he rented a room. It has been impossible to find out from where he got the money to pay his rent. He made no attempt to find any sort of work, and began frequenting the Royal Milk-bar which is well-known to the police as a breeding ground of juvenile crime. There is little more to say about him except that he has wilfully refused all offers of help. Sir, I would refer you to his so-called statement which he dictated to me in the Receiving Home. It will give you an insight into his character.

The bastard as dobbed me in good an proper. What statement? Ee wanted me to talk about meself, an I obliged im. Now I get it flung back in me face. Can't trust any of these so-called welfare officers. They'll do yuh in as soon as spit at yuh!

Well, I ave to bear this, this cross. No way of gettin out, not with that big cop guardin the door. Well, I don't care. Let em do their worst!

Their worst is to get me to condemn meself outa me own mouth. The magistrate gets me to stand, an like Robinson ee gets me talkin. What do they expect, that I'll break down an beg forgiveness. Knew a bloke who used to do that, but ee ended up inside too. So don't give em the satisfaction of seein ow scared yuh are. Naw, yuh can take it, like a Swan kid!

MAGISTRATE: You say in your statement that you do not believe in God?

'Yeah, that's right.' (A nudge from Robinson makes me remember the 'sir'.)

'Yes, that's right, sir!'

MAGISTRATE: And so you have no time for such things as the bible and oaths made before God, or this court?

'No, I don't . . . sir!'

MAGISTRATE (*with a smile*): And so, we may presume that you'll swear to tell the truth on your honour?

What is ee gettin at? I shrug, but another nudge from Robinson, makes me realise that ee wants an answer. Well, what else to say, but 'Yes, sir!'

MAGISTRATE: Well, we'll have to take that on good faith, won't we?

Is words scare me, frighten me to ell an back. They out to get me, an suddenly I don't wanta be got. I blurt out just like the frightened kid I am inside: 'Sir, couldn't find no job. No matter what ee says, couldn't find no job. Ad no money either. Ad to pay me rent, ad to eat, ad nuthin to live on, or for!'

MAGISTRATE: Mr Robinson was there for you to appeal to. Did you?

'Im! Ee wouldn't elp me if I was dyin.'

MAGISTRATE: And these articles of clothing that are on the table. I suppose you were going to sell them for food and shelter?

'Me own gear was dirty an outa fashion. Me mates expect me to dress sharp.'

MAGISTRATE: Oh. . . . Now remember that you have given me your word of, of honour to tell the truth. This is very important. Do you feel any remorse for the offences you have committed?

'Dunno, what that is. I was ungry, the rent was due, an I needed some dough.'

MAGISTRATE: I think that we have heard more than enough. Mr Robinson will you come here please.

To ave ope was outa the question. I didn't know what they would do to me. I watched that cunt Robinson an that Magistrate whisperin together an knew me rabbit was trapped. Still, I didn't believe that I would get eighteen months, but I got it. A bloody stupid kid gettin eighteen fuckin months in Freo. That was what they were like! . . .

So milk-bars ave some pretty rotten memories for me, though I did meet Denise in the Royal, an she was never rotten, though maybe I was by then. Aven't seen er since that time long ago, that time I went into the milk-bar an found Chinky there. We ad got out together. Ee ad talked of goin straight, of keepin outa trouble, an ere ee was in the place which was trouble. We came together. Ee ad a

small bottle of rum an we drank it while ee talked of this
yorga that ee loved an who ad gone off with someone
else, or didn't want im without any moola. One or the
other. Who cares! It set im up for the job I ad in mind, for
I wasn't goin straight without any dough. I ad to make
some before thinkin like that. If yuh ad dough yuh could
go to the eastern states an far away from ere. Without it
yuh were more or less just out on parole waitin for em to
pick yuh up when they felt like it. No escape, bradda. It
was like that.

An so we talked over dreams an then over plans. An
Chinky listened. It was a good enough job. I remembered
from one of me childhood busts that a shop ad a big safe
in it an, as nuthin ever changed in those one orse towns,
that safe would be sittin there waitin for us. I ad learnt
what to do with safes in boob. Yuh put the thing in the
boot of a car, drive out into the bush an bash the back
open with an axe, then bob's yer uncle. Easy, an the car?
Rip one off in the city. The town was only a few ours
drive away. We could do the job in a night, then be away
with all that lovely money. Sounds good, doesn't it? Most
jobs do — in words, though rarely in the actions. Well,
this one followed the pattern. We fucked it up real good,
an I fucked meself up real good for too many years. Still I
wrote this book usin it, an they're makin this movie usin
it, so after all I mightn't ave fucked it up altogether. It
just took some time to get the proceeds — an Yankees pay
real good for scripts an book rights. So bob's yer uncle,
mate!

Me conclusions cheer me up no end. That old job
payin off now. I settle back to ave a good perve on Ernie
an Jinda makin out in the only love scene in the movie.
Of course it's done in the nude, an Jinda as a beautiful
body. Not the garden of Renee's, but still lithe an strong
an young — though er tits are on the small side. I can see
all of er as Al re'earsals the scene. These women ave no
shame, or Ernie for that matter. Both of em aven't got a
stitch on.

They got this small size bed all lit up. A camera to the

side an one peerin right down on em to catch the action.
Not only this, but there's a mike angin over'ead to catch
the slightest grunt. Man, I couldn't get it up, not with all
that gear around, not with all those eyes peerin, not with
those cameras an mike ready to take it all down in sight
an sound.

Ernie stands there with a scowl on is face. Ee ain't likin
it either. Jinda is more cool. She knows she as a fine body,
an stands straight an tall as if she's wearin clothes, unlike
Ernie who unches up like ee's ready to protect is watch-
amacallits, is private parts from loomin publicity. Kev,
ee don't elp matters by callin out: 'Yuh two, yuh look
like two plucked chickens.' Not only Ernie, but the
director shoots evil faces at im an ee olds is peace. The
scene's been re'earsed a couple of times an been mucked
up a couple a times, what with Ernie not avin is eart, so
to say, in it. True, bro, the things yuh gotta do in the
movie business, like flashin yer moom an muniyin in
front of everyone, even though it might be just pretend.

DIRECTOR: Ernie, baby, this is it. Put your brain in your
prick. You've been in the slammer for months, and are
aching to get your rocks off. Come on, this'll be a take.
Remember you've got a hardon on as solid as Mount
Rushmore. On the bed, that's right, just follow through,
no words, only sighs, grunts. Jinda you're great. Right,
action. That's it, that's it, good, good. Now again, this is
a take!

Ernie stands there naked. Ee looks down at the lovely
body of Jinda spread out just waitin for im. Ee flings
imself down on er in rage, anger an lust. It's vicious,
abrupt an over in a sec. No messin about with the 'I
love yuh' business.

DIRECTOR: Cut, that's it. Knew you could do it, Ernie.
Ernie doesn't say a word. Ee gets off the bed an pulls
on is clothes, looks around with a mad glint in is eyes,
then shouts: 'Fuck this!' an rushes off.

DIRECTOR: Temperament, temperament, he'll cool off and be back in no time.

Me, I'm not so sure. There comes a time when yuh've ad enough of em playin with yuh, of em eyeing yuh off as if'n yuh were some animal. Ernie's reached that stage, an we should go an find im before ee shoots through, movie or no movie. That's ow it appens amongst us, but the Yank ee don't know us an our ways.

I look around. Jinda is decent again. I think of askin er to come with me to find Ernie. I am about to go to er when this old bloke who's to play the old man in the movie taps me on the shoulder. Is names Winjee Tailor an ee's just arrived this mornin an as bin in the movie business since Aborigines stood posin on one leg an lookin yer noble savage for the camera. I must admit ee looks the part too. As a long white beard an air. Ee dresses in out-of-date safari suits with flares an as badges on is lapel to show the world that ee belongs to various Returned Servicemen's Clubs around Australia. Although ee as only bin in town a day, ee as managed to score a Perth an Freo one. All in all, when I met im, I knew that ee was perfect for the part. Ee as that, ard to describe, weepy manner which some of the oldies ave, an if that comes over in the picture, it'll be good for our image. Now I watch is face as ee stops to make sure that ee as me attention before wastin words. Ee begins in is soft voice with just a suggestion of a sob, or sadness be'ind it.

WINJEE: Yuh know, I've met many a young bloke like Ernie. They think they got the world on a string. Everythin's goin their way, then sumthin appens, suddenly like a shower of summer rain. Yuh know, one minute the sun is shinin, the next the skies clouded over an it's rainin cats an dogs. Might las the res of the day too. Might las for a long time. It appens like that to our people. Dunno why, but it does, an if they don't pull through, if'n they don't get elp, it might be the end of their career. They throw it all away jus like that, just over sumthin which as bin nigglin em. They don't feel it at firs. They might try to get away from it by drinkin. They might try to work arder, but it's in em an keeps growin an growin. Then one day, just like now, sumthin snaps inside an they rush off, an next day yuh might fin em ome, or even in another state. That's where Ernie is at. Ee's at that stage. We better fin im an talk im roun.

I agree with Winjee. I know that feelin. Yuh gotta keep movin, or yuh gotta do somethin, or other. So we leave the filim mob an go out to look for im. If it was me the first place I would look would be in a pub, but it's not me, it's Ernie, an so at a loss, we go to the milk-bar just on a chance. Ernie's sittin there unched over a cup of coffee in a booth. Winjee takes a seat beside im, an I go to get us both a cuppa tea. I catch the conversation as I come back.

ERNIE: I dunno, Uncle, yuh know, I've ad it what with all those cameras an eyes on yuh. Can't stand em lookin at me. Take off yer clothes, get it up, do yer stuff, yuh an actor so don't protest. Professional, what're yuh bein paid for? It's nuthin, everyone does it now, then yuh think of yer mum, or yer lations watchin the scene, an it its yuh sudden that they mightn't like it, that they'll tell yuh that yuh shouldn't do that on the big screen, in front of everyone, that yuh should feel shame. Yuh know ow it is, you bin in filims long enough.

WINJEE: Boy, I was with Mick Jagger in that Kelly flick. Ee did is job quiet an when it was over ee left. Yuh know, I bin in bout an undred pictures now — most of em walk-on parts. Yuh know, they need an Abo for the job, an get in touch with me agent, or at first ask roun an fin me. A lot of the parts were bad, yuh know rubbish! Member this one part I ad. Stockman part. Must've bin a bit like the blacks were treated on em stations. It was 'Jacky do this, and Jacky do that' all through the flamin picture. Yuh could see that the director ated blacks. Well, one day I ended up feelin like yuh did today. I ad ad enough of this picture, an all I wanted to do was pack me swag an be off. It was like that I was feelin, an it was in the old days when we couldn't even ave a few beers to relax on. It was in the bush, an that night after the shootin I went out for a wander. I went along, yuh know, just like the boy in this picture, an all at once what with the stars above an the quiet of the bush about, all me problems fell away, disappeared into the earth. I felt me gut relaxin, an, yuh know what, I did that filim, stuck it out an felt proud for stickin it out. . . .

'Yeah,' I say, breakin in, 'an the shootin in the city is just about over. Soon it'll be in the bush an more relaxin.'

I go on to say more, somethin about the nude scene bein the only one in the movie, but a fierce look from Ernie stops me. Ee must be thinkin 'Who is this bloke to give me advice?' — so I go silent, an let the old man continue on in is weepy voice — a voice full of knowledge an enough experience to bring Ernie around, at least I ope so. I check out the milk-bar while I wait for the result. Ere we shot a scene today. A scene when I or Ernie ad just got outa jail. It's strange now, becomin stranger. I can't begin to capture that scene, feel it as if it's from me own life. It flickers there, an it's like it as nuthin to do with me any more. It's to do with Ernie an Jinda. Is face is right there in front of me, angry an disillusioned — 'Seventeen, seventeen, just turned seventeen. Graduated and got that twist, at seventeen, at seventeen.' An Jinda is there too. Er face outa focus, some'ow unclear, uncertain, as if ow she lives is the only way, an there is no thought of changin it.

It was when I ad got out that time an reached the city from the port. I went to a mate an got me a clothes' change. I ad to look sharp, an so I went to this old mate an borrowed some a is clobber. Ee couldn't say 'yes' fast enough to get rid of the jail stink. I got into a black shirt an black jeans with pink outlined pockets an, last of all, a pair of crepe soled desert boots. This shoulda made me feel good enough to face the world. *Look out, look out! Ere ee comes, the black cat slinkin,* but I didn't feel nuthin, nuthin at all cept that tight ball of pain an anger in me gut. It felt so tight it urt. It almost doubled me over, but I was a Swan boy an ad to swagger, an ide all that.

Well, I swagger into that milk-bar as if I own the place, stop right in the middle of it an let me eyes drift round. Trouble is I'm feelin outa place, feelin that I ad never bin in the milk-bar before in me life. I am feelin like that, then luckily a voice moves me outa me funk.

VOICE: Ey man, when did they let yuh out?

'Today, mate. They ad to do it — too tough for em to old.'

ANOTHER VOICE: Ow's Chinky, ee's bout due out too?

'Ee split to see is folks. Reckon ee'll be along before the night is through. Yuhs all family to im, same as yuh are to me.'

VOICE: Yeah, an ol Poncee is still the one with the goodies.

'Good, could do with some cheerin up. Too bloody long I bin away, too bloody long.'

An that's ow it went. The next step would've bin, yeah, go to the jukebox an put on a rock'n'roll record. The music ad some bite then, rebel music condemned by the rich an Frank Sinatra, fuck im! An after that to ol Poncee for a plateful of sandwiches an some of is red, red wine. Ee is friendly as ever, but warns me not to make trouble as ee fishes up a bottle of grappa or some such piss, an tells me to put it under the table so that ee can make believe that it isn't there. Ee makes me pay fore ee gives me the bottle and sandwiches. I take em an go an sit at me table right at the back. No one'll bother me there, an I can get pissed while listenin to the latest its. I must've bin feelin bad, an felt worse when I ad ad a couple of cups of Poncee's evil wine. It was just when I was feelin that suicide was the only way out, just like a lot of us feel sometimes, when Jinda, no Denise came up to the table with er azel eyes an warm manner that even I could feel was for real. Some'ow she made me feel special — sometimes.

DENISE: Hi, cuz!

'Yuh know ow it is, first day out is one big long celebration. Soon I'll be able to see me freedom double up, or nuthin.'

DENISE: Yuh put that song on: 'A Waitin Time'. It's bin me favourite.

> Waitin for you, waitin for you,
> A waitin time of passin time,
> Waitin for you, waitin for you.'

'Yeah, glad to see yuh too. Bin a waitin time for me, but time passed as slowly as a earse.'

DENISE: Yeah, that's ow it is in those places. Me sister just got outa Fairly the other day, true? Yuh wouldn't believe ow she felt.

'Glad to ear that she's out. I wouldn't lock me worst enemy up.'

DENISE: Yuh know, I missed yuh sumthin awful. Even thought of joinin the Salvoes to get inside to see yuh, true!

'I can just imagine yuh bashin away at that old tambourine. All the cons would've loved it. Yuh wanna a drink, got a bottle of Poncee's grappa under the table. Can't get through it all by meself, not after bein locked away for so long.'

DENISE: I'll just ave a sip outa yer cup. Betta watch out, those cops ave started checkin the place out about this time. A couple of demons.

'Fuck all detectives, fuck em all, the long an the short an the tall.'

DENISE: True, but keep yer voice down. Yuh only got out today.

'True, but who the fuck cares if I'm in or out?'

DENISE: I do, cuz, I do. God, this stuff's awful. No wonder yuh down in a dumps.

'Not, first day out an I'm celebratin.'

DENISE: So celebrate with somethin better. Ave a few of these pills, they get me through not only the days, but the nights. They give yuh a lift an keep yuh up there. Right, got em down? They'll sober yuh up in a flash, true! Get em from this Bungyi man. Ee's okay that one. Wish there was more like im.

'Yeah, there's always the good ones, so's I've eard. Never met one though. They all like that Robinson bloke. Sweet on the outside, bitter on the inner.'

DENISE: Just old on, an those pills'll it yuh for a six. I'll go an put some music on.

'Ey, I'm feelin great. You know, up there where I belong' . . .

An so's that's ow Denise lifted me outa meself that time, but she ad to use pills, an then er charm. Winjee's different. Ee uses charm or somethin close to it, an Ernie is listenin to im.

WINJEE: Yuh actin with me now. I'll keep an eye on yuh. Just follow it through. It ain't no big deal. I've done it undreds of times. Bin in so many of em that I can't count em. Yuh know me part in the picture. It's only us two inna scenes. We'll be doin em together. Just follow me lead an it'll be all right. I gotta a script ere. We'll just look it over. Sometimes I can't understan some a the words an need a little elp.

Ernie an Winjee are soon engrossed in me script. I'm outa of it again, but as I look at Winjee I know ee's perfect for the part. Ee'll just be a poor bloody black in a bush scene, but not just any poor bloody black, but someone who as bin to places an done things. I can see im now. See im as clear as I see that old man I ad in me story. It was after we ad mucked up bustin in a that store. Chinkee ad run towards the car an I ad run into the bush. Walking down a track. First grey glow of dawn begins spreadin from the orizon an out through the bush. Shadows of a tree. Movement there. Fling up rifle. Wait. Muzzle pointin at that tree. Waitin, scared, move backwards not takin eyes offa that tree. End with back against stump on other side of track. Watch as old man comes out onto track. Stops.

OLD MAN: Yuh look just bout done in, boy?

'Got lost, bin walkin most of the night.'

OLD MAN: Need a spell. Camp's there.

Old man turns off the track. Esitate, follow im. Glow of fire through trees. A clearin. Stop. Eyes move. Oval gunya made outa branches, paperbark an essian sackin. No one, cept old man at the fire. Throws on more sticks. Flames blaze up around blackened billy can suspended on a wire stretched between two upright sticks.

Squat opposite old man. Watch is black cracked ands.

OLD MAN: Feed an a sleep'll set yuh to rights.

Old man at shelter. Kneelin at entrance. Ead inside in the gloom. Tense. Withdraws with tin plate an spoon. Returns to fire. Stirs billy can, tips some of the contents onto plate. Passes it across.

OLD MAN: Yes, Jessie's boy!

Stop eatin. Tense.

'Naw, first time ere. From the city. Yuh bin there? Might've seen yuh there?'

OLD MAN: Yuh in trouble?

'Me middle name, but this time I'm only lost. Came out after a roo, an missed me way.'

OLD MAN: Knew yuh grandmummy. That old woman bin of me tribe — tribal sister she was. Yuh know, she get to call me bradda just like real bradda. Yer mummy, she watchamacallit, daughter, somethin like that, but she go to mission school an forget everythin. . . .

'Thanks for the tucker. Where does this track lead to?'

OLD MAN: Yuh see yer mummy lately, boy?

'Naw, but she's in the city.'

OLD MAN: No she not. She come back ere. Sick, an come back to er people.

'She ain't got no people ere. She always told me that she came from another town.'

OLD MAN: She from ere, an she back ere now — with er people.

'Where?'

OLD MAN: In the Noongar camp. She at ome there.

'But, but she never ad anythin to do with Noongars. An she kept us away from em too. Always fightin an carryin on. She didn't want to mix with any of em. Well, well — oh serve er right! Er an er ideas of tryin to be white. Oh ell! . . .

OLD MAN: Better get some sleep. Get a fresh start in a mornin. Warm beside the fire.

Lie on blanket ee gives. Rifle beside me. Restless, twistin an turnin. Daylight. Clearin empty. Get up rifle in and. Go to gunya, look inside. See a cracked cup. Pick it up an shake it. Rattle of coins. Empty the cup an pocket the money. Check the clearin.

III
OME

NINE

Panorama of the camp
The clearing, deserted. Winjee enters. Holds a stick from which dangles half a dozen rabbits. Dead. Sings an old bibbumum song.

Winjee (singing):
> *Dandara wantum me,*
> *Dandara wantum me,*
> *Boojoor me counteree,*
> *Ngora walla kuttijee,*
> *Boojoor me counteree,*
> *Dwonga walla kuttijee.*

Goes to fire. Puts down rabbits. Goes to gunya. Pokes head inside.

Winjee: *Bin to the traps. Got some meat.*

Leaves the gunya entrance. Ernie crawls from the gunya. Apprehensively gets to his feet.

Ernie: *Got to get moving. . . .*
Winjee: *Long way to go, son. Maybe too far, maybe not? Best to get some tucker into yuh.*
Ernie: *No time, Granddad, no time!*

Winjee sniffs at billy can, ignoring any sense of hurry.
Nods, tips rest of stew on to tin plate. Passes it up and
across. Ernie sits down. Begins eating.

Winjee goes to the gunya. Pokes a hand inside, feels
around. Pulls out a knife. Ernie gives a start. Winjee
picks up a rabbit. Begins skinning it.

Looking down at the old man. Ernie puts down
plate beside him. Winjee puts the freshly skinned
rabbit on it. Grabs another. Looks up. Stops his work.

Winjee: *Wait! Got a few bob for yuh. Might get yuh
back to the city?*

Ernie with open mouth. Eyes flicker in guilt.

Winjee crawls into the gunya and comes out with
the empty cracked cup.

Ernie's face sags, recovers, hardens, sneers.

Winjee looks at Ernie.

Ernie's lips begin quivering. He seems about to
burst into tears. Face turns away to hide emotion. His
hand fumbles into his pocket. Brings out a handful of
coins. A few fall as his hand moves out.

Winjee: *Son, keep it. No need of it out ere, an it might
get stolen, or sumthin. Best you keep it.*

Winjee begins skinning the rabbit. Begins humming
the same song as before. Pulls the skin off the rabbit
and looks up.

Winjee: *Ear that song before?*
Ernie: *Dunno . . .*
Winjee: *Tell bout your country. Ow it can give yuh an
and when yuh need it. It just like yer mummy, yuh
know?*
Ernie: *Yeah . . .*
Winjee: *Yeah, yuh gotta listen. Ear it whisper. It
knows yuh, son!*
Ernie: *Yeah, but I gotta go. . . .*

Winjee claps his hand under his rib cage.

Winjee: *Yuh keep it ere all the time. Keep it right ere. Yuh know that?*
Ernie: *Dunno . . .*
Winjee: *All yuh young'uns gotta keep on the move these days. No listen to nuthin. Just keep movin.*

Gets to his feet. Pulls down a waterbag hanging from a tree. Takes it and hangs the cord over Ernie's shoulder.

Winjee: *Blackfella never forgets is water, just like ee never forgets is dreamin. Get goin! An keep to the bush. It knows yuh!*

Walking away from the camp site. Looking back to see the old man. Old Wally looking smaller an smaller.

Never saw im again after that. Me mum useta say that ee was outa is ead. But that time, I didn't find im like that. An I did feel better after meetin im. Things changed. I knew that I ad to face what I ad done. Knew I ad to, but didn't know ow to finish it off. Ow do yuh end a story, moonlight an roses, or ashes an sackcloth? Let im end it im self. It's is story, after all. The above was ow it was in the script, an more or less ow Al shot it. I watched im goin over the scene carefully. Yuh knew that this was goin to be a piece of exotica for the Yanks. At least Winjee looks the part, an knows ow to play the role. Ee does ave that touch of sadness to bring all the wisdom out. It was a good scene, but the last of Winjee, as Al's bin mutterin, at least someone told me, bout budget overruns, an all that. Yeah, we know what budget overruns are, an so we do our bits nicely, an everythin clicks, an Winjee's role is over. That's ow it is in the movies.

An there's not much left to be done. We approachin the end of the filim, an the end of the work too. Just the kid's scenes to go, an it'll be over cept for the editin an all the rest that Al does to get it into final shape. We get on the ired bus to go back to the town. We bin filimin by the side of the road, an ad built a nice little gunya to make it native. Looks good too, though lonely now that we leavin it. Some careless bastard as left the fire burnin. I old up the bus. Get down an go to it. Check to see if there's any chance of it gettin outa control, say a goodbye to the lonely camp site, then get back on board. Sit with Winjee an tell im what a great job ee done. Stop the bus on the outskirts of the town an get off. I've ad enough filimin for today an can go an see a lation. Me mum an er mum were old drinkin buddies. She sure was sad to ear that mum ad passed away. Just as I was sad to ear that er old lady ad passed on. Old Wally of course ad gone long before em. Yeah, most of the oldies are gone an we're becomin the oldies. Well that's life, fada!

Mary still lived in the same old ouse. All wood an lookin somewhat ragged round the edges. It should look that way. Mary ad ad a brood of kids an the ouse adn't ad much ope with em around.

'Ey, Mary, ow you bin keepin? I'm with the filim mob what's come down ere to make that filim of me book. They usin some of the kids from the school, an that means a bit of extra money.'

MARY: Ow ya going? Eard yuh were in town. It was me that picked out the kids for yuh. We got the smartest ones. Just let me know if they misbe'ave emselves?

'Do that. Yuh know one of the parts is about the time I met yuh an the mob at the stockyards. Yuh know the time I killed that rabbit?'

MARY: Oh, that time. I was just a skinny girl livin under a bush. Yer lot lived in an ouse like the Jacksons.

'Yeah, but fat lot of good it did us, that ouse!'

MARY: So long ago. It's comin back to me though. God, Andy's gone, so's Bill an Fred. Only us two left outa that lot.

'Can't last for ever, I suppose. Yeah, us mob usta play on those stockyards.'

MARY: Runnin along tops of the rails. The silo was

best though. Slidin down those great piles of wheat. Bad an stupid though. Bill got smothered doin it. Appened just when you were taken to that Swanview Ome.

'Didn't ear about it for a year. Must've bin about ten or eleven then?'

MARY: The littlest of the mob. Yuh trailed after us all the time. We usta run whenever we saw yuh?

'Yuh didn't!'

She sinks into reminiscences, an I sink into memories an regrets. I wanta be that kid again. I wanta play with those kids again. I wanta be free an easy. I wanta kill that rabbit again. I want to! Too many bitter memories an me mind shies away, then recovers. I don't wanta kill any rabbit. Too much of a rabbit in me own life for that. Let the bastards live. Me mind collapses into an image, an I see Clarissa as me mum starin at me an sayin:

'You bin muckin round with those Noongar kids, aven't you? You ave, aven't you?'

I see me self standin there dumb, then Clarissa makes that statement of what appened to me. 'You want to stay with me, don'tcha? Well, keep clear of those kids, you ear me. I don't want you goin like me other kids.' Clarissa appears about to break into tears, then with a sniff recovers.

This vision is enough for me. I don't trust what Al is doin to me script. Got to keep an eye on im, but then I wait for a cup of tea, an forget about it. So much as bin changed that it ain't a true story any more, but then it never ad bin. It's just a book, just a filim like any other one, but if it's like that, ow come I feel so bad about the changes made? Dunno, maybe I want to put people in it I like an know? Maybe I want to ave a record of ow it was when I was a kid? It means somethin to me. I know that now!

TEN

Stand on the roadside an look towards where me ome usta be. Ain't there no more. Just a eap of bricks, just a fadin memory in me mind of ow it used to be those many long years ago. Now the ouse is gone, me mum's passed on, an me near kin, me bradda and me sisters ave scattered all over the state. Not much of me left ere any more. Used to live in that eap; used to play in that paddock. Ad an old dead tree in the middle of it. Must've bin made into firewood a long, long time ago. Remember ow I used to play in a corner of that paddock. Playin in the mud, buildin me kid's dreams into mudpies of night-mares. Yeah! Remember playin in the dirt one day. Just a skinny kid messin around in the dirt. I pokes me foot deep into the earth, an it stings. Not the earth though, whiteman's rubbish — broken glass. I jerked me foot away from the sensation. It wasn't pain, just a sorta of unpleasantness. I look down, an the sole of me foot slashed open clear to the bone. Can remember even now lookin down at the skin slashed open to show a lotta blue things inside. Got the scar on me right foot to prove it appened. I yelled out as the blood begin comin, an limped towards the ouse. Me mum came to the back door an began runnin towards me. Then I was in er arms as she carried me towards this old shed that was at the back. She scooped out some cobwebs from the rafters, or roof beams, an plastered em on the wound. The blood stopped flowin an the achin stopped. It didn't urt an I could've stopped me snivellin. Didn't though, me snivels grew into sobs that racked me skinny body. Strange though, it wasn't from the pain, or the shock. Only that, only that I wanted to stay in me mum's arms forever an a day. Yeah, but er arms was weak an couldn't protect me. That old nightmare kept comin back, an then the look an feel of that rabbit too slow to run. Yeah, too urt to run, but ee was a grown man by then an not a kid with a bit of the devil in im, just as a lot of Noongar kids ave it in em. . . .

The house as it was in the old days.

A single light burns in the bare kitchen. A big old wood stove glows in the middle of the side wall. A scarred kitchen table and a couple of chairs fill most of the space. Half of the table serves as a stacking place for the dishes. A tin basin sits among them. It is filled with water and dishes are soaking in it. The only light comes from the red glow of the stove and from a hurricane lamp set on the other end of the table away from the dishes. It illuminates Clarissa and a boy of nine. They are eating slices of bread and dripping. An enamelled pannikin of tea is in front of them both. Suddenly, they look up and freeze. A large policeman stands in the doorway. He holds a heavy flashlight in his hand. He plays it around the kitchen illuminating its poverty.

Policeman: *It's about the boy!*
Clarissa: *Me boy's done nuthin wrong. Ee's a good boy!*
Policeman: *Someone got into Cox's store and pinched some things. . . .*
Clarissa: *Ain't im, ee's too small an skinny.*
Policeman: *Just have a look around, that'll settle the matter.*

The Policeman's seen enough of the kitchen already. He walks past the sitting mother and boy and enters the other room. Through the doorway the foot of a big bed can be seen. The woman and the boy stare through the doorway apprehensively. The policeman returns. He has a grimace on his face. He holds some comics, a pair of sheets and a dress.

Policeman: *Thought so, I'll be back tomorrow.*
Clarissa: *You not goin to take im like you took the others? Ee's the only one left to me.*
Policeman: *You lot shouldn't have kids. At least he'll be looked after where he's going.*

The mother grabs her son. She begins crying. The boy begins crying. The policeman leaves.

Policeman (from the door): *Just don't go bush!*

The mother tightly hugs her son staring out into the night through the open door. The torch's beam flickers across the dark space. It hits the mother right in the face. She reels as if struck. The boy begins screamin: No, no, no!

Exterior of a darkened yard behind a building. Late night.

The yard is filled with stacks of drums. Ernie crouches behind a pile of drums. He has a rifle. He aims the barrel towards the source of a flickering torch beam. Suddenly, the beam hits him. Blinded he pulls the trigger. The rifle goes off. The beam of light jerks spasmodically. Sound of the torch hitting the ground. The light goes off. There is a groan and the thud of a body hitting the ground.

Ernie (screams, as the boy had): *No, no, no!*

He runs, clambers over the gate of the yard and into the street. He turns away from the town and runs into the bush.

Bush exterior, Mid morning.

Ernie is walking down a bush track. Suddenly the bush goes silent. A dog barks from behind him. He darts off the track. Hides behind a bush. Darts back to the track and begins to run along it. The barking gets louder and louder. Ernie whirls, his rifle coming up. The dogs rush at him. A rider gallops up. A second breaks through the scrub. Ernie hesitates.

Voice of second rider: *Drop that rifle, you!*

The rifle falls to the ground. The rider gets off his horse and picks it up.

Policeman: *Taking you in for attempted murder. Lucky for you it was.*
Ernie: *Yuh mean I didn't kill im?*
Policeman: *What do you think?*

He puts the handcuffs on Ernie's unresisting wrist. The youth stares down the track.

Ernie: *I didn't kill im?*
Policeman: *Naw, just a scratch.*
Ernie: *I'm sorry, I didn't mean to do it.*
Policeman: *Yeah, now move!*

He pulls Ernie to the side of the horse and clips the other handcuff to the stirrup iron. He gets into the saddle, whistles at the dogs, and starts off down the track at a canter. Ernie runs beside the horse. The group gallop off and into the distance.

CREDITS BEGIN OVER BUSH SCENE.

DIRECTOR: This'll make the movie, man. Beautiful, real beautiful. They'll love these bush scenes in the States. I've got a sixth sense about these things, you know. Poetry and sympathy for the underdog are where it's at, and that means the Australian bush for sure: the real Australia just like our Old West.

Ee's talkin to is self. No one is listenin after the last cut. Ee might like the bush, Yanks might like the bush, I might like the bush, but the others, Eastern Staters don't. Too ot an dusty for em. They load the gear on the truck in double quick time. We all pile into the bus, an fore we know it we're on the way back to the pub where we puttin up. Could tell a story or two about that pub. Begin to cast me mind back, but Ernie who as slumped into the seat beside me (guess this actin business is ard work), turns an angry face at me. I try a grin, but the face still scowls. Dunno what's wrong with im. The filim is alright, isn't it?

ERNIE: That fuckin end, bro?

'That fuckin end? Al done it more less as I wrote it. Not like some of the other parts. Never a word from yuh bout em — cept that nude scene.'

ERNIE: Well, yuh ended it wrong, yuh did. All yuh got is another blackfella endin up in jail. Nuthin good about that. Shoulda ad im shoot it out with those blokes on orses. An not only that, but ee says ee's sorry. Sorry for what they done to im, that's a joke that is?

'What do yuh mean? What sort of endin did yuh want? Once I thought of doin it this way: He doesn't shoot anyone, just gets away. Ee doubles back into town, steals a car, makes it back to the city, an uses the money to make it to freedom in the east. What do yuh think of that?'

ERNIE: Better than the one I just did.

'Old on a sec, aven't finished yet. Ad another endin too. I liked this one a lot. Bit like the movie, so I'll put yuh in the role, so yuh can easily follow it. Yuh an Jinda do the job. Yuh both take rifles. The cop gets it an yuh off into the bush. Yuh both meet Old Wally, I mean Winjee an, after yuh leave im, you ear those dogs an then orses gallopin towards yuh. Yuh get be'ind a fallen log. Wait for those dogs, wait for those orses an men to reach yuh. Yuh both got yer rifles, an they is waitin too, waitin for those policemen. . . .

'But it didn't appen like that, didn't! Yuh should go to jail, mate an' feel what it's like. It eats away at yer guts. Well, yuh shoot a cop, an what sorta sentence do yuh think yuh'll get? Six months to get yer arse in. Well, the bastards gave me *The Governor's Pleasure*. Is pleasure alright! They throw away the key an yuh got to please that Governor to be let out. So what do yuh do? Inside all yer life, or give in a little — a lot — to get out. That book was me ticket to the outside, bradda. It ad to please em, so the endin was an appy one for em. Little Jacky so sorry for shootin the policeman — well, Jacky was sorry cause ee was in Freo for an eternity an a day. So ee wrote that book, nice white social workers elped im, an the reports went in, an the book got written, then published. I was an, what do yuh call it, an exemplary prisoner, an so after a dozen years or so I was let out. Bin out ever since. So now yuh know why the endins like that. It ad to appen, it was as it appened — at least to em!'

Ernie mumbles somethin an goes silent. Well, there ain't many ways to skin a rabbit, but I found one an used it. Better than what a lot of those other blokes inside do with their time an energy. So who cares ow ee feels. I ad to end the book like that, didn't I? Well, I did, didn't I? Rabbits ave to find a way to live too! . . .

ELEVEN

Ernie an me stagger down that street in Freo. I ave the spraycan of paint in one and, a tinny in the other. Drain the beer, an fling the can away. It rolls along the street as if a dust devil ad pounced on it. The paint isses out into two foot igh words:

KILL US WHITE AUSTRALIA IF YOU CAN.

Then that police car comes rushin down the street to send us scuttlin down that alley an doublin back on our tracks an through the gates of Freo. Safely ome? Like fuckin ell!

Ernie turns to me when ee gets is breath an says: 'Betcha this is the first time crims took refuge in ere?'

'Dunno about that, bro, dunno bout that.'

That's ow this daydream ends durin the end of filim party we're avin in the pub. It's rowdy with us. Dunno what the locals think, but we aim to ave a good time. Fuck em! Ernie is at me side, an suddenly I turn to im. A line comes straight outa that daydream to it im in the face.

'Well, I ad to teach yuh ow it was like. I ad to, yuh know?'

'Teach, what? — to say "sorry" to cops?'

'No, ow yer so fuckin stuffed up inside, that yer so fuckin fucked up outside, that yuh'd do anything to be in the bush avin a drink with yer mates.'

ERNIE: Dunno bout that. It takes a road to whine, a train to cry. Yuh can't give em the satisfaction.

'Satisfaction, what satisfaction? — yuh think they give a fuck bout you. They got yuh, bradda, an they don't care bout yuh any more. Yuh ave to give a little to get a lot.'

ERNIE: Yeah, but yuh ave to give a lot to get a lot, yuh know? If no one knows what yer on about. If all they see is that black man down, that's the end of it. But if they see im up there, fightin an comin through, they'll know it's for real, they will. Yuh gotta get away from all the bullshit. Get rid of it an then, if yuh give a lot, they'll know that it's for fuckin real, not just bullshit.

'Yeah, an when yuh locked in that cell an it's Christmas time too. You lie on yer bed feelin the Christmas plum duff a lump in the belly just ready to ache. Yeah, yuh lie on the bed, listen to the feet of the screw rattlin along that metal landin. An the ole in the door flickers for an instant with an eye, then the lights are switched out, an yuh lie there knowin that not even yer mind is free, but it's in boob too. The only Christmasses yuh can remember is in the Ome. They might've bin good, if yuh ad anything to judge em with. Yuh got better food, an a balloon to blow up, an maybe even a toy to play with — but yuh were still in some sort of jail. Ow to get out, ow to?! Yuh'd promise the devil yuh soul for a night in is ell.'

ERNIE: Just like in this picture, too much fuckin talk! . . .

'Talkins cheap for both of us.'

ERNIE: Yeah, but I'm fed up with it.

'Well, the filim's over, yuh can enjoy yerself on yer wages.'

ERNIE: Yeah, buy a load of bullshit an spread it over everythin. . . . Too much fuckin smoke in ere, too much fuckin noise too. Goin outside for a bit. Wanta come along?

'Naw, this is yer life. Yuh always mix with this mob. This is the last night for me.'

ERNIE: See yuh.

'See yuh.'

I get meself a fresh can, take a gulp, an exchange it for

a coke. Start on the ard stuff a little later. But the other's
are right into it by now. Don't feel in the mood, but then
never say 'no' to a free beer, or tucker for that matter, so I
forget the coke an pick up the can. Beside me the camera
crew are uddled in a group—an they talk bout black-
fellas not mixin! I stay there for a while close to another
can, an ear one of em say: 'God, you can't count the
number of shots that Yank stuffed up.' An another replies:
'Well, it's just about over now.' A third adds: 'Yeah,
thank God. We'll finish it before it finishes us. That
bloody Yank is high tension.'

'Yeah, but ee does it the Yankee way, not the Aussie,' I
butt in, then pass em each a can before movin on. Just
spotted Jinda lookin for someone, an maybe it's me.

She's ain't, she's lookin for Ernie. Doesn't disappoint
me anyway as me feelins are elsewhere. Tell er that I was
just talkin to er Ernie, an that ee went off in a funny
mood. She looks concerned, an leaves me to go an look
for im outside. Call after er not to ave a look at me ome
town under the full moon.

'Yuh might see some ghosts,' I yell, then go back an get
another beer.

The film tecs are still discussin the fuckups of 'the
Yank', so I leave em to their whingein. Al as begun to do
is prime trick for the night. Ee begins to juggle is balls.
Suddenly, there is a sound like a shot. Ee misses one of
the balls, grabs, an the other two fall an roll away. There
is the sound of a car engine roarin, then the screech of
tires tearin off. Must be the locals avin a bit of fun?

Al recovers an groans: 'My God, what am I doing
amongst you Aussies anyway?'

'Makin a movie, makin money,' I yell.

AL: I sure did, I sure will.

KEVIN: Yuh ear bout this old bloke. Ee ad this boomerang. The most returnin one in istory. Always came
back to im. Used to go around the pubs, see this white
fella, come up to im and say: 'Yuh wanta buy a real
boomerang from a real blackfella?' Of course the white

bloke looks at this old fella, sees that ee's the genuine
article alright, and offers to buy it. No igh prices though:
10 or 12 dollars. Well, this old bloke accepts, gets the
money in is and, then tells the white bloke that ee's got a
boomerang throwin exhibition to put on that mornin,
or evenin, or what ave yuh. 'Meet yuh ere, first thing
tomorra,' ee tells im, an is away before the bloke realises
it. Yuh know, ee ad that way bout him —

'Al, dolls, great film, great director,' a voice grates
across the end of Kev's story. Clarissa, lovely lady of me
first night's wet dream, lunges forward an enfolds Al in a
strong pair of black woman's arms. I can almost feel is
bones creak, but the amount of beer ee's put away keeps
im inflated. Ee doesn't even blush, or feel shame, when
she begins beltin out:

> It's a long way from New York City,
> He's a long way from home,
> He's a long way from New York City,
> An the sweetest life he knows.

They all take it up. Well, if we're goin to ave a sing
along I might as well get into the act. As soon as they
stop, I begin:

> Freo jail, boys, Freo jail,
> I left all me buddies
> In freo jail. . . .

Doesn't fit into the general mood of rejoicin an me
voice trails off. Guess I'm feelin the need for another of
Kev's funny stories to brighten me up. Instead I get
Clarissa with er body pressed against me side. Need a
song to sing bout er. Better than singin about some
crummy jail. I flop me arm around er an give er an ug.
'Ain't no ugs in Freo jail.' I push the line away an
concentrate on the freedom beside me.

'Bin waitin all week,' I tell er.

'Honey, you know how it is now. Lines and upheavals.
I not only had to act in the thing, but I had to see that it
ran smoothly. You could've helped, you know?'

'You didn't ask me.'

'Do you have to be asked to do everything?'

'Yeah, at least once.'

'Well, anyway, Al thought your script was *absolutely* marvellous.'

'Yeah, but ee changed a lot?!'

'That's how it is in the industry.'

'I'll remember that.'

'Anyway, it is marvellous. The really first Aboriginal film script and film.'

'Yeah,' I agree, not knowin if I agree, or not. Then suddenly, I remember it's just ow I wrote me book. Ow I ad written it to comfort em. This is what Ernie ad meant. Maybe I shouldn't ave changed it, maybe I should ave written a different script? Oh, who the fuck cares!

An so I grin an agree, but thinkin of Ernie puts me in a mind to see Ernie, an I shout: 'Ey, where's the star of the show?!'

An Kev shouts back: 'Can't be far, is dog's still ere.'

I look at Kev, then catch sight of Renee who's standin there lookin more than a bit embarrassed. She's with Kylie. She catches me eye an flashes from shame to smile in an instant. She beckons with er glass at the bar. I lift me can in agreement, find it still alf full an gulp it down.

'Yuh know, I might catch yuh tonight,' I say to Clarissa droppin me arm off er shoulders. 'Yuh free?'

'Maybe, honey,' she drawls, then begins singin: 'Maybe, honey; maybe honey; If you've got the money; to come along with me.'

I laugh an leave to 'later, honey'.

Renee is never pissed, but tonight she's showin an edge. Bout time too.

'Have you seen Ernie,' she asks with the same note of concern in er voice that Jinda ad ad.

'Last time I seen im ee was off to get some air.'

'What time was that?'

'Who knows ow to tell the time at a party? Anyway Jinda went off to look for im. I wanta ave a drink with im too.'

'I bet she went off after him. The bitch!'

'Ey, steady on, they cousins after all.'

'Yeah, kissing cousins.'

'Yuh see that old Elvis movie too on telly the other night?'

'What old Elvis movie?'

'Kissin cousins!'

'Oh God, not the jokes.'

'Everyone believin in God tonight. Clarissa just told me that Al thought me script was okay.'

'It was. It was really good in parts.'

'Maybe? What d'yuh think of the endin?'

'Ernie was perfect in it.'

'Ey, I got this idea for another filim. Yuh see there's this Aboriginal guy. Ee tries to ighjack this plane. Protestin over the Bicentennial Celebrations. Well, not really, yuh see ee's a little simple, an this guy grabs im, puts these ideas in is ead. Well, that's that part, the other part is yuh. I can write it around yuh. Yuh see yer the hosty on the flight an yuh save the day. What d'yuh think of that for a script?'

'Well? . . .'

'I bin watchin ow yuh stand an things like that. It's easier to fit a person to a part, rather than a part to a person.'

'Do you think so?'

'Yeah, if I ad a known yuh before I wrote the script, it woulda bin a different girl yuh played. A nicer one. Then I like beatniks. See yuh still got yer gear on. Might become a new fashion after this filim. Come outside an I'll recite yuh some poetry.'

'Poetry?'

'Yeah, beatniks love poetry, an yuh look so much the beatnik, besides there's the full moon an a river close by. We could go there an look at the water, or for Ernie, or somethin.'

'It is a bit stuffy in here.'

'Another thing, this is me ome land. Tell yuh a bit about that river.'

'Yes, let's get out of here. Clarissa's just about to start

one of her country and western songs. It's going to be "Wasted Days and Wasted Nights" for sure.'

'She's got a fine voice.'

'Yeah, but the song. Let's go. Fill up my glass for me, won't you?'

'Take a can. There's a law against drinkin in public, yuh know?'

'Careful, the boogy man might get you.'

'Come on!'

I'm gettin a little angry bout all the fuckin praise an blame I'm gettin tonight. Yuh do yer time, an that's it. But it ain't, yuh gotta get over it, or come out under the full moon in a Western Aussie warm night with just a touch of the breeze to move the air of the girl beside yuh. Whatever anyone says, this is livin. Man, this is life, an not that rottenness inside.

There's still the park at the side of the pub between it an the river. It's kept nice and tidy with a statue of a digger in the centre surrounded by flowerbeds. Al would love it for its Australianness. Ee would see that; ee would see the river, but not the story markin out this spot as special.

'Yuh know,' I begin, as we sit on a bench facin over the dark river waters. 'They don't know it, but just near the bridge is a sacred site. Site of the Rainbow Snake. Yuh know about the Snake?'

'Yes, there was a series on television called that.'

'Well, ere's one of its sacred sites. Is what d'yuh call it, is essence lives down there. Yuh know, *Uluru* in Central Australia is one of is eyes, the other is the moon, an if yuh just look at the water, just listen to it, is body'll come up into the sky. Yuh'll see is ead takin shape too.'

'Arrh, you're having me on, aren't you? You are a bit of a con man. I've been watching you.'

'Not about things like this. Ey, there's old Al an Kev gettin some of the moonlight.'

Director an trainee director stagger arm in arm towards us, then veer away at the last moment.

AL: Beautiful, beautiful! A dark river, a full moon, a park, a boy and girl sit on a bench. They don't make films like that any more, they sure don't.

KEVIN: An appy endin, the Kooris would go for it.

AL: But no money in it, old boy.

KEVIN: Come on, an I'll shout yuh another drink. It's free tonight.

AL: But only if it's a martini.

KEVIN: Come on, I'll tell yuh a yarn bout this Italian chap as we go along.

AL: No, this time you're going to listen to one of my stories, a Jewish story. You see there was this Jewish group that had been meeting for years to study the Talmud. That's, well, say like your Christian bible. One of these guys had got into the habit of bringing along a flask of brandy to sip from during the meeting. One night in the excitement of the discussion he overdid it. He ended up dead drunk. Passed out. Well, his buddies decided to give him a lesson. They carried him off to a cemetery. Laid him out alongside one of the graves and left him there. A few hours go by. . . .

Is voice fades away in the distance. Their backs lurch towards the door of the rowdy pub. As they enter across the screen grows a uge

'THE END'